BRITISH MEN OF SCIENCE

General Editor

Sir Gavin de Beer F.R.S. F.S.A.
membre correspondant de l'Institut de France

William Herschel

WILLIAM HERSCHEL

Angus Armitage

Thomas Nelson and Sons Ltd

London Edinburgh Paris Melbourne Johannesburg
Toronto and New York

THOMAS NELSON AND SONS LTD
Parkside Works Edinburgh 9
36 Park Street London W1
117 Latrobe Street Melbourne C1

THOMAS NELSON AND SONS (AFRICA) (Pty) LTD
P.O. Box 9881 Johannesburg

THOMAS NELSON AND SONS (CANADA) LTD
91-93 Wellington Street West   Toronto 1

THOMAS NELSON AND SONS
18 East 41st Street New York 17, N.Y.

SOCIÉTÉ FRANÇAISE D'ÉDITIONS NELSON
97 rue Monge Paris 5

63-780

Printed in Great Britain by
Robert Cunningham and Sons Ltd, Alva

Preface

In the following pages I have tried to re-tell the story of the life and labours of William Herschel. There is no lack of documentary material upon which to base an account of Herschel's career; and the romance of the self-taught amateur's rise from obscurity to world-fame, almost literally in a night, has attracted numerous biographers. Here, however, the emphasis must be placed upon his scientific achievements rather than upon his fortunes; and I have restricted the biographical portion of the book to a brief outline so as to devote most of my allotted space to explaining the discoveries and ideas which Herschel unfolded in his seventy scientific papers. In summarizing these papers it has seemed best to depart from the chronological order of publication and to group them according to subject; but I have tried to preserve the sense of the development of Herschel's thought, particularly in those fields of investigation in which he was pre-eminently a pioneer. The introductory chapter is intended to establish the historical context of Herschel's work and to indicate some of the problems that he found awaiting solution. And in the concluding pages the attempt is made to gather up the threads of his long discourse and to show how they have been woven into the fabric of modern astronomy.

The remote depths of space which Herschel was the first to scrutinize still exert their fascination upon the astronomers of our own day. The greater 'space-penetrating power' of modern telescopes has not invalidated his conception of the physical Universe as an unbounded space sown far and wide with quasi-galactic systems of stars. But of late the search has been intensified for some broad trend in the apparent distribution of all these 'island universes' which may help to decide between the rival theories now dividing the suffrages of cosmologists.

Herschel never received the mathematical training that most of his contemporaries in astronomy had undergone; and the branches of the science which he established, or which he laboured to advance, were all capable of development, at least as far as he carried them, without any elaborate mathematical technique. This simplifies the writer's problem of communication; and I hope that the explanations I have attempted of the astronomical and physical phenomena, problems, and procedures with which Herschel was concerned may serve to make the book intelligible and useful to the students and general readers for whom it is intended.

This is the appropriate place to return thanks, as I gladly do, to all who have afforded me help or copyright facilities in the preparation of this book: in particular, to Mrs E. D. Shorland, the representative of the Herschel family, and to the Syndics of the Cambridge University Press, for permission to quote from documents printed in Lady Constance Lubbock's *Herschel Chronicle*; to Miss Susanna L. Fisher of the National Maritime Museum and to Dr W. H. Steavenson, F.R.A.S., for information kindly supplied; to the Councils of the Royal Society and the Royal Astronomical Society, the Royal Greenwich Observatory, the Science Museum, the National Maritime Museum, the Yerkes Observatory and the Mount Wilson and Palomar Observatories for permission to reproduce illustrations as indicated; and to the Editor of the Series, Sir Gavin de Beer, F.R.S., for his helpful interest and advice.

A. A.

Acknowledgments

Plates 13, 19, 20, 22, 23, and 24 are reproduced by courtesy of the Mount Wilson and Palomar Observatories; Plates 4, 5, 8, 10, and 11 by courtesy of the National Maritime Museum; Plate 12 by courtesy of the Royal Greenwich Observatory; Plates 7, 14, 15, 16, 17, and 18 and Figure 12 by courtesy of the Royal Society; Plate 6 by courtesy of the Royal Society and the Royal Astronomical Society; Plates 1, 3, and 9 by courtesy of the Director of the Science Museum, London (Crown copyright reserved); Plate 21 by courtesy of the Yerkes Observatory.

Contents

List of Plates

List of Figures

Chapter 1

Herschel's Heritage of Astronomy

The life and work of William Herschel form an episode in a story which began in prehistoric times and which is still being unfolded today. It is the story of how, through the ages, Earth-bound man has scanned the heavens from afar, penetrating by sight and thought ever farther into the depths of space. Astronomy is one of the oldest of the sciences. Behind the complex pageantry of the skies there lie certain regularities and recurrences which early man found it important to grasp and to systematize. And by the time his battle for bare survival had been won, the contemplation and interpretation of this element of order in celestial phenomena had begun to afford intellectual satisfaction to those who had the taste and the leisure for such things. Gradually the earlier star lore became a science as we understand the term today. This introductory chapter is intended to provide a brief outline of the growth of the science of astronomy up to Herschel's time with special reference to those problems which chiefly claimed his attention.

We are apt to regard astronomy as somewhat remote from ordinary human interests, in contrast to such sciences as physics, chemistry, or biology, the practical value and economic importance of which are more obvious. Living for the most part in great cities, we see but little of the changing face of the sky. Celestial observations are, indeed, vaguely understood to be indispensable for time-keeping, for navigation by sea or air, and for large-scale surveying; and there is an increasing recognition of the contributions made by the astronomer to the progress of modern physics. But these facts are vividly brought home only to the specialists directly concerned.

It is different with primitive societies: their day-to-day life is so closely bound up with the periodicities of the heavens that they usually possess a rudimentary knowledge of astronomy even if it falls below a strictly scientific level. By their vicissitudes the Sun and Moon regulate food-producing activities. The month brings back the moonlight nights when hunting is opportune; the year defines the fertility-cycle of the crops and livestock of the settled farmer. These recurrent periods are measured out by the circuits regularly performed by Sun and Moon against a background of stars which it was the task of the primitive astronomer to group into picturesque constellations, serving both as a celestial system of reference for the motions of the larger luminaries and as guides to the mariner and the pathfinder. The stars appeared to be scattered over the inner surface of a great sphere which rotated about the observer, carrying the Sun across the sky in its diurnal course, and so defining the fundamental period—the day—in terms of which the month and the year were expressed. To the same background of stars were referred the erratic courses of the five star-like bodies which we call Mercury, Venus, Mars, Jupiter, and Saturn: they were all discovered in prehistoric times, we know not by whom. The ancients classed them with the Sun and Moon to make, in all, seven planets or 'wandering stars'. They travel slowly, night by night, through the constellations of the so-called 'fixed stars' so as to make complete circuits of the heavens, each in its own characteristic period. The month and the year constituted two alternative systems of reckoning time, affording a basis for the calendars, lunar or solar, indispensable for performing agricultural operations and observing festivals in due season, keeping historical records, and so forth.

Something approaching a scientific system of astronomy arose in ancient Babylonia among the priestly schools of the last three centuries before Christ. This development may well have been prompted by the practical need for a working relation between the rival lunar and solar calendars. It bore fruit in numerical tables inscribed upon clay tablets and specifying the motions of the Sun, Moon, and planets corrected for characteristic variations in their rates of travel at different parts of their courses, which all fell within the great celestial belt of the zodiac. Babylonian astronomy was deeply imbued with mythological ideas and closely associated with the belief in astrological prognostication. The Greeks, too, started out from prevailing superstitions; but they soon adopted a predominantly naturalistic attitude to phenomena. By applying their own geometrical technique to data derived from the Babylonian ephemerists, they originated the tradition of scientific astronomy which, by a somewhat circuitous route, has come down to us.

The Greeks mainly taught that the Earth is a sphere fixed at the centre of a finite, spherical universe; that the orbits in which the Sun, Moon, and planets appear to revolve round the Earth are each compounded of a few uniform circular motions; that the stars are fixed like studs to a crystal sphere, and that such phenomena as comets and meteors arise from the combustion of vapours in the Earth's atmosphere (cf. Fig. 1). A few Greek thinkers standing outside the main tradition anticipated later views, such as that space is infinite and our planetary system a transient concourse of atoms; that the Earth rotates daily on its axis, and that it revolves with the other planets round the central Sun. But the more conservative Greek conception of an Earth-centred universe was established in the Hellenistic period by Hipparchus of Rhodes (second century B.C.) and Ptolemy of Alexandria (second century A.D.). Hipparchus compiled the earliest-known catalogue

Fig. 1 The medieval conception of the universe (according to Peter Apian, ca. 1530) showing the Earth composed of successive layers of earth, water, air, and fire, the concentric spheres carrying the Sun, Moon, and planets, and the sphere of fixed stars.

of stars, the position of each upon the sphere of the sky being defined by specifying a pair of angles in somewhat the same way as a place on the Earth is given by its longitude and latitude. Hipparchus also established the practice of classifying the stars according to their brightness to the eye, his system of stellar *magnitudes* serving as the basis for all subsequent classifications of the kind down to our own day. He classed some twenty of the brightest stars as being of the first magnitude while those just visible (to the naked eye) were deemed to be of the sixth; the intermediate magnitudes represented what were judged to be equal gradations of apparent brightness. Ptolemy embodied all this earlier work, with his own geometrical scheme of the planetary motions, in his historic book the *Almagest*, which retained its authority for some fourteen centuries.

Greek astronomy reached medieval Europe as a literary tradition, partly transmitted through the civilization which the Arabs had established on the borders of Christendom. The practice of celestial observation was revived in the fifteenth century; and in the sixteenth century Copernicus formulated his own conception of a Sun-centred planetary system which, in its broad outlines, has been adopted by the modern world. Thus it was almost universally accepted in Herschel's day that the Sun was the central body, that the Moon was a satellite of the Earth, and that the remaining five planets, with the Earth as a sixth member of the planetary band, revolved round the central Sun. The unravelling of the precise laws of planetary motion derived from the assiduous observations of Tycho Brahe, extending over the later years of the sixteenth century, and the patient analysis of these observations by Johannes Kepler at the beginning of the seventeenth. The Italian scientist Galileo Galilei prepared the way for the physical explanation of the planetary motions by sweeping away the unsound ideas on mechanics which had come down from antiquity. Isaac Newton formalized the principles of the new mechanics, and he generalized the familiar phenomena of terrestrial gravity into a universal attraction between material particles. He thus laid the foundations of a system of gravitational astronomy which, built up by the Continental analysts of the eighteenth century, served to account for most of the intricacies

B

in the courses of the Moon and planets and received its classic formulation from Herschel's great contemporary Laplace.

Galileo was a pioneer also in the application of the newly invented telescope to astronomy. The telescope is essentially an instrument for forming a magnified image of a distant object. It serves also to collect a lot more light from the object than would enter the pupil of the unaided eye. In the type of telescope employed by Galileo the light is refracted through a convex lens (the object glass). Galileo employed a concave lens as an eyepiece; but the more advantageous practice of using a convex lens, or lens combination, with which to magnify the image soon established itself. Employing telescopes of his own construction, Galileo discovered several previously unknown celestial phenomena to which William Herschel, in due course, was to direct his more powerful instruments—the mountains on the Moon, the dark spots which appear fitfully upon the bright disc of the Sun, four of the little moons which revolve about the planet Jupiter, the Moon-like phases of the planet Venus, and the mysterious appendages to the planet Saturn. Galileo's glass also significantly revealed that the luminous girdle of the heavens called the Galaxy, or the Milky Way, consisted of innumerable faint stars.

Telescopes of the kind employed by Galileo and the early seventeenth-century observers suffer from certain optical defects, the images showing coloured edges; and Newton discovered that these arise from the fact that ordinary light is made up of a multitude of differently coloured beams which are not all brought to the same focus by the object glass of the telescope. Acting upon a suggestion made by James Gregory, he constructed a different type of telescope in which the image was formed by reflection of light from a concave metal mirror, or *speculum*, and which was free from the defect in question. Telescopes of this kind are called *reflectors* to distinguish them from the *refractors*, in which the image is formed by refraction of light through a lens. Both types have been in use since the time of Newton. Herschel's preference was for reflectors; and his lifelong experience in their construction and use was of great benefit to the subsequent development of that form of telescope. The optical dimensions of a telescope are indicated either by stating the *focal length* or the *aperture* (the diameter) of its object glass or speculum. Focal lengths are generally given in feet; apertures are usually expressed in inches; there should be no confusion between them in what follows. Telescopes are normally equipped with a graduated series of eyepieces differing in magnifying-power.

Following Newton's explanation of the optical defects of the refractor, investigations were set on foot which, by the middle of the eighteenth century, had led to the 'achromatization' of the instrument by using an objective consisting of two lenses made of two different kinds of glass. However, Newton's classic experiment with the prism has proved to be of much greater significance to astronomy than simply as explaining a fault in the refracting telescope and indicating its cure. The manifold developments in astronomical spectroscopy mostly occurred after Herschel's day; but he was one of the first to pay attention to the spectra of stars, and one of his greatest achievements was the discovery of heat radiations refracted beyond the limit of the visible spectrum.

We cannot by direct observation estimate the distance of a heavenly body from us, or the relative distances of two or more such bodies. But for many astronomical purposes it is convenient and sufficient to regard a star or a planet as located somewhere upon the surface of a vast 'celestial sphere' of indefinite radius and of which the observer occupies the centre. We can then readily estimate the angular separation of two such objects: it is the angle subtended at the observer's eye by the arc joining them upon the conventional sphere (Fig. 2). Most of the early astronomical instruments and techniques were designed for measuring such angles. And about the middle of the seventeenth century the telescope began to be applied to confer a greatly increased degree of precision upon these

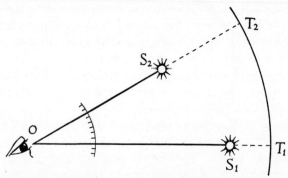

Fig. 2 The angular separation of the stars S_1 and S_2 is given by the angle T_1OT_2 which their projections T_1, T_2 upon the celestial sphere subtend at the eye O of the observer.

traditional instruments. Telescopic sights, restricted in their sweep to the plane of the meridian and employed in conjunction with the newly invented pendulum clock, served for the fundamental measurement of time and for the precise location of stars and planets upon the celestial sphere. Sometimes two stars lie so close together in the sky that they can be seen in the same field of view of the telescope; their angular separation can then be measured very precisely by means of a micrometer placed in the focal plane of the instrument. The standard form of micrometer, invented in the seventeenth century and still in use today, consists ideally of two parallel wires or threads, one fixed, the other movable by turning a screw with a graduated head (cf. Fig. 3). The wires are set at right

angles to the line joining the star images, with the fixed
wire crossing the one star image and the movable wire ad-
justed to cross the other; the separation of the stars is then
read off in turns and fractions of a turn of the screw, these
arbitrary units being afterwards converted into seconds of
arc. Herschel often employed this type of micrometer, but,

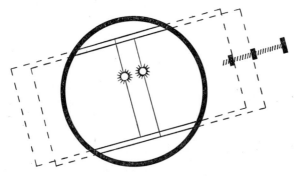

Fig. 3 Use of the micrometer to measure the angular separation of a close pair of stars.

as we shall see, it did not completely meet his needs, and
he was the inventor of other ingenious forms of the instrument.

The fundamental determination of time and of the
positions of celestial bodies became the main preoccupation
of the great national observatories of Paris and Greenwich, established in the 1670s; their recorded observations
served as the foundations for much of the dynamical astronomy of the eighteenth century. For the unravelling of the
interwoven courses of the Sun, Moon, and planets depended primarily upon accurate determinations of the
positions of these objects upon the sphere of the heavens at
stated times; and when at length the mechanical principles
governing the motions of these bodies had been grasped,
all the available resources of mathematics were called for
to establish that these principles did in fact account for al-

most all the intricacies of the lunar and planetary orbits.

Herschel made no perceptible contribution either to fundamental observation in this sense or to celestial mechanics. He was not a mathematician; and he never installed the 'fixed instruments', as they were called, required for that type of observation. However, his researches touched the main historic tradition of astronomy at many points; and he was frequently dependent upon information supplied to him by professional astronomers, notably by Nevil Maskelyne, the contemporary Astronomer Royal. It was in 1675 that King Charles II had established the Royal Observatory at Greenwich and had conferred the title of Astronomer Royal upon John Flamsteed, its first Director. Flamsteed's principal achievement was the construction of a catalogue giving the positions of some 3,000 stars as determined by telescopic observation. Of this star list Herschel was to make extensive use, although he discovered that it was not as accurate as had been supposed. Flamsteed's successor at Greenwich, Edmond Halley, announced in 1718 that, in the course of the centuries, three of the brightest stars appeared to have changed their positions in the heavens; he thus opened up an important field of investigation which early attracted the attention of William Herschel.

There were two other problems of stellar astronomy under discussion when Herschel started upon his career as an observer of the heavens. One was of two centuries' standing, and concerned the detection and measurement of an elusive optical phenomenon which *ought* to be perceptible on the Copernican hypothesis of an annual revolution of the Earth round the Sun, and the discovery of which would furnish a long-sought proof that the Earth does in fact so revolve. In the strict physical sense the phenomenon had nothing to do with the stars; but it bore upon stellar astronomy in another way as affording a means of determining how far distant the stars are from the Sun and its train of planets. How could an eighteenth-century astronomer hope to find the distances of the stars, and why was this problem tied up with the hypothesis about the Earth's annual revolution?

It is a matter of everyday experience that, whenever we move, stationary objects around us appear to us to move in the opposite direction and the more so the nearer they are. Viewed from a railway carriage in motion, a steeple on the distant horizon and a tree in a field near at hand both seem to drift towards the rear of the train; but the tree drifts the more rapidly, and in a few moments it may appear to pass from the right side of the steeple to the left. Such an apparent shift in stationary objects, resulting from an actual displacement of the observer, is called *parallax*; and the apparent change in the relative positions of two such objects which are at different distances from the observer is called *differential parallax*. Now an observer whom the Earth carries round the Sun once a year should see a periodic parallax in the positions of the distant stars, though he is in the situation of a pleasure-seeker on a merry-go-round rather than of a passenger in a railway carriage. And the early astronomers were well aware that if they could detect such an annual stellar parallax it would prove pretty conclusively that the Earth revolved round the Sun and would establish the scientific truth of the Copernican theory. At the same time the accurate measurement of such parallax in a star would enable the astronomer to determine that star's distance from the solar system as so many times the Earth's distance from the Sun and hence ultimately in miles or in some other more convenient unit. In much the same manner do surveyors find the distance of an inaccessible object (such as a tree on the far side of a river) by taking its bearings from each end of a measured base-line (Fig. 4).

One way of detecting parallax in a star is to measure, from time to time, the elevation above the horizon at which the star crosses the meridian: parallax should cause this elevation to vary slightly from month to month while

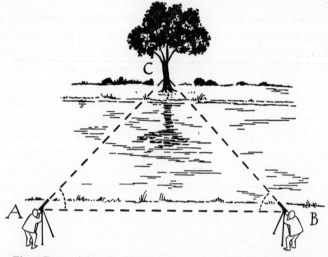

Fig. 4 Determining the distance of an inaccessible object. The distance of the tree can be calculated when the base AB and the angles at A and B are known.

restoring it to its initial value after the lapse of a complete year (Fig. 5). Robert Hooke in the seventeenth century, and James Bradley in the eighteenth, both selecting the same star (Gamma Draconis), looked for such a variation in its meridian altitude, but neither of them succeeded in establishing it, though Bradley was confident that had the parallax amounted to as much as one second of arc he would have detected it. Upholders of the Copernican theory were somewhat embarrassed by such failures; but they could argue plausibly (and, as the event proved, correctly) that the stars were at such vast distances from us that their (correspondingly minute) parallaxes were too small to be detected with the instruments available.

That was broadly the position when Herschel first directed his attention to the matter.

The second problem in stellar astronomy under discussion about the middle of the eighteenth century concerned the arrangement of the stars in space. The stars, as we saw, were formerly supposed to be attached like silver studs to a rotating crystalline sphere of which the observer occupied the centre. This view of them was adopted by Aristotle and his medieval followers, and, as a conventional

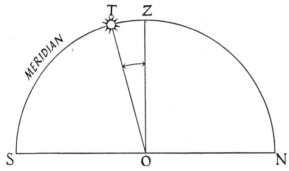

Fig. 5 Annual parallax exhibited by the star T should cause its meridian zenith distance ZT (or its meridian altitude ST) to fluctuate slightly in the course of one year.

assumption, it still suffices today for many of the purposes of geometrical astronomy. By the end of the sixteenth century, however, it had begun to be suspected that the stars, which differ so markedly in brightness, might be at different distances from us. They might be distributed in depth so as to occupy a layer of space having a definite thickness, or they might even form an assemblage extending outwards from the Sun to infinite distances in all directions. The Italian philosopher and arch-heretic Giordano Bruno, writing about 1580, pictured the stars as suns (of which our Sun was a typical specimen), each travelling freely through space accompanied by its train of inhabited planets. And twenty years before Herschel was born, Edmond Halley, as we have seen, discovered indications of such 'proper motions' in certain of the brighter stars.

The stars do not appear uniformly scattered over the sphere of the heavens. Besides tending to form clusters here and there, they crowd towards the luminous belt of the night sky which we call the Milky Way or Galaxy, and which Galileo's telescope showed to consist, in fact, very largely of faint stars. Various fanciful explanations of the Galaxy had been suggested through the ages; but in the middle of the eighteenth century an obscure amateur astronomer, Thomas Wright of Durham, published a book in which he maintained that the stars constituted an orderly system and that conclusions as to the structure of the Galaxy could be drawn from the observed distribution of the stars upon the celestial sphere (*An Original Theory or New Hypothesis of the Universe etc.*, London, 1750). Wright grasped the essential idea that the reason why the stars appear crowded together in the Milky Way is not that they are really concentrated into a ring, but that the region occupied by the stars extends farther in all directions in the plane of the Milky Way than in the directions perpendicular to it. He supposed the Sun to occupy a roughly central position among the stars, which are scattered at random (in 'a kind of regular Irregularity of Objects'), so that the Milky Way arose as an optical effect due to the observer's looking through a greater thickness of stars in some directions than in others, and to his having no sense of the different distances of the stars which his vision encountered and which he projected indiscriminately on to the background of the sky (cf. Pl. 2). Wright conceived the stars as suns, each attended by a train of planets and comets controlled by its gravitational attraction which, however, did not extend to neighbouring stars and their systems; and he thought that the barely perceptible 'cloudy Spots' or nebulae, visible here and there in the heavens, might well be 'external creations' (separate systems of stars independent of and bordering upon the one we inhabit). Wright's theory remained generally unknown to the astronomers of his day; but a short summary of his book, published in a Hamburg periodical, came to the notice of Immanuel Kant of Königsberg, then in his late twenties and working as a private tutor, but later to become one of the greatest philosophers of all time. Kant never saw Wright's book, but he was inspired by it at second hand to elaborate his own theory of the constitution and evolution of celestial systems, which went far beyond the merely descriptive aim of the Durham astronomer.

Early in 1777 Alexander Wilson, the first Professor of Practical Astronomy at Glasgow University, found himself discussing with his son Patrick why the stars do not fall into one another under their mutual attractions. They sought to solve the problem by asking why the planets do not fall into the Sun. Here the explanation evidently lay in the 'projectile forces' of the planets, which maintain them in 'periodical motion' about the luminary; and the stars may similarly be preserved from 'one universal ruin' by revolving about the centre of the 'Grand System of the Universe' (as Alexander Wilson wrote in his anonymous *Thoughts on General Gravitation etc.*, London, 1777). It is of interest to note that Thomas Wright in his *Original Theory*, which, as we shall see, partly anticipated Herschel's cosmology, had written twenty-seven years earlier of the 'projectile, or centrifugal Force, which not only preserves [the stars] in their Orbits, but prevents them from rushing all together, by the common universal Law of Gravity' (p. 57). Wilson may have been acquainted with Wright's little-known work; but Herschel nowhere in his writings refers to Wright, though much of his early manhood was spent in Wright's countryside. And he seems not to have seen Wilson's tract until he received a copy from the author a few days before he published his paper of 1783. He acknowledged it in a note appended to the paper and in a letter to Wilson.

To sum up, until the age of Herschel astronomers had concerned themselves almost exclusively with the motions, mutual relations, and surface features of the Sun and its family of planets and satellites. The stars they had treated as mere geometrical points upon a conventional sphere, requiring only to have their positions catalogued and mapped with all needful accuracy so that they might serve as pointers for the measurement of time and as markers for defining the locations of the Sun, Moon, and planets. But now stellar astronomy was about to enter upon a new phase in which a star would be regarded as a physical object possessing individual characteristics of position, of motion, of intrinsic brightness (constant or variable), and, in due course, of much else besides—as possessing, too, an evolutionary history and as associated with neighbour stars through a common origin and a parallel development.

Chapter 2

Herschel's Life Story

In memoranda which he wrote down from time to time
William Herschel placed on record the chief events of his
early life, while the journals and memoirs of his sister
Caroline, and surviving letters to and from the Herschels,
serve to chronicle the astronomer's later years. William
Herschel could trace his ancestry back to the seventeenth
century when his great-grandfather, Hans Herschel, kept
a brewery at Pirna, a town in Saxony. The second son of
Hans was Abraham, who worked as a landscape gardener
near Magdeburg; and Abraham's third son, Isaac, became
the father of the astronomer. An uncertain glimpse of an
older generation is afforded by letters which William
Herschel received in 1790 and in 1819 from a distant
cousin. These letters tell how three brothers named
Herschel, persecuted for their Protestant faith, migrated
from Moravia to settle in Saxony. One (the writer's
ancestor) made his home at Schmilka, another in Postel-
nitz, and the third (from whom the astronomer was des-
cended) in Pirna.

Isaac Herschel was born in 1707. He, too, worked for a
time as a gardener; then he turned to music and, having
learnt to play the oboe, he joined the band of the Hanoverian
Foot-Guards. When Hanover became involved in the War
of the Austrian Succession, Isaac Herschel accompanied
the Foot-Guards as a bandsman through the campaign

which culminated, in 1743, in the defeat of the French at
Dettingen by a mixed English and Hanoverian force under
King George II. In 1732 Isaac had married Anna Ilse
Moritzen, whose family belonged to Neustadt, near
Hanover. They had ten children of whom six reached
maturity. We shall be chiefly concerned in the following
pages with the life and work of the second surviving son,
Friederich Wilhelm, who was born in Hanover on 15
November 1738 and whom we shall henceforward call
William Herschel, the name which he adopted when he
settled in England and by which he was naturalized in
1793. Closely associated with him in his labours and in his
fame was his younger sister, Caroline Lucretia, born on
16 March 1750; brief mention will also be made of the
astronomer's elder brother Jacob (1734-92), and of his
younger brothers Alexander (1745-1821) and Dietrich
(1755-1827).

The children received their early education at the
Garrison School; but they were given further instruction
by their father, who also introduced them to astronomy.
William Herschel later recorded how 'my father's great
attachment to music determined him to endeavour to make
all his sons complete musicians, and . . . my father taught
me to play on the violin as soon as I was able to hold a
small one made on purpose for me' (*Scientific Papers*, I,
xiv). And from Caroline we have the reminiscence: 'My
father was a great admirer of astronomy, and had some
knowledge of that science; for I remember his taking me,
on a clear frosty night, into the street, to make me acquainted with several of the most beautiful constellations,
after we had been gazing at a comet which was then visible.
And I well remember with what delight he used to assist
my brother William in his various contrivances in the
pursuit of his philosophical [scientific] studies' (*Memoir
and Correspondence of Caroline Herschel*, 7f.).

At the age of fourteen William joined his father in the regimental band as an oboist (Jacob was already a member); and in the spring of 1756 all three accompanied the Hanoverian Guards to England where the regiment was to be temporarily stationed as a precaution against the threat of a French invasion. The months of garrison duty were spent in Kent, where William found time to learn English; and the Herschels were received into local musical circles, making friends who were to be of great assistance to the two brothers when, a year later, they returned to England to seek their fortunes. Jacob now obtained his discharge and returned home; and by the end of the year the whole regiment was back in Hanover.

In the spring of 1757 the Foot-Guards were involved in a campaign against the French, an episode in the Seven Years War, which ended disastrously for the Hanoverians at the battle of Hastenbeck, William and his father sharing the hardships of the fighting-men. William had joined the regimental band at so early an age that he had not been formally enlisted, and his father advised him to leave the service, undertaking to obtain his discharge from the commanding officer. A formal document has been preserved: signed by General A. F. von Spörcken and dated 29 March 1762, it regularizes the young oboist's withdrawal from the forces of King George II. The French having occupied Hanover, William made for Hamburg; here he was joined by his brother Jacob, and late in the autumn of 1757 the two young men crossed to England and made their way to London. Meanwhile the Hanoverian forces went into captivity; but two years later, in 1759, the French were defeated at Minden, the prisoners were set free, and Isaac Herschel returned home in peace.

William and Jacob Herschel arrived in England almost penniless; but thanks to the recommendations of the friends they had made on their former visit, they managed

to establish themselves, William by copying music and
Jacob by taking pupils. They also took part in concerts and
stayed during the summer months with some of their
Kentish acquaintances. In the autumn of 1759 Jacob returned to Hanover to become one of the Court musicians.
William sped him on his way with all the funds that he
could spare. He had begun to wonder whether his prospects
would not be brighter in the provinces, where competition
was less severe; and in 1760 he gladly accepted an appoint-
ment as bandmaster of a regiment of militia of which the
Earl of Darlington was Colonel and which was just then
quartered at Richmond in Yorkshire. Herschel, however,
terminated this engagement in the following year to work
as a free-lance musician at a succession of north-country
centres—Newcastle, Pontefract, Leeds, and Halifax
(where he acted as organist after the settlement of a law-
suit to remove the organ as a 'heathenish thing'). He was
now regularly composing music; and notes of his activities
during the years spent in the north country record the
completion of numerous 'symphonies' and other pieces and
his appearance at concerts, which enhanced his fame. At
one of these concerts he was accompanied on the violon-
cello by the Duke of York, brother of King George III.
And when Herschel led an Edinburgh orchestra in a performance of some of his own works in a St Cecilia's Hall
concert (the earliest public concerts in Britain), the philosopher David Hume was present and later invited the
young composer to dine with him. In the spring of 1764
Herschel visited his family at Hanover; this was to be his
last sight of his father, who died three years later.

Despite the hardships of this precarious, wandering life,
and the strain of incessant musical performance, teaching,
and composing, Herschel pursued, during his early years
in England, an ambitious course of self-education. He per-
fected his knowledge of English; he learned Italian (the

The Georgian Planet with its Satellites.

Plate 1 Sir William Herschel. A pastel portrait by J. Russell, 1794.

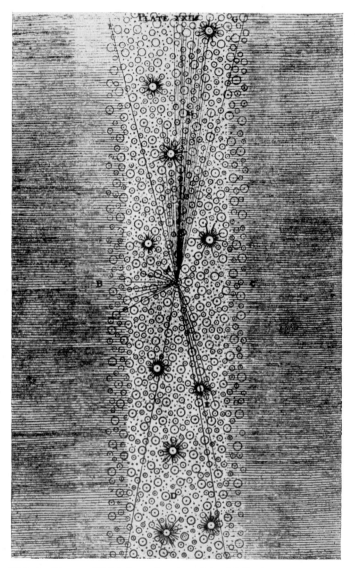

Plate 2 Thomas Wright's explanation of the Milky Way as an optical effect of the Sun's central position in a stratum of stars.

musician's language), and he made considerable progress with Latin. Greek he soon abandoned as leading him too far from his favourite studies. He made profitable use of every moment of leisure; and his son, Sir John Herschel, could recall having often heard his father relate how once, when he had been reading on horseback, he found himself standing in front of the horse with the book in his hand, having been tossed over the animal's head.

After nearly ten years of this unsettled existence, Herschel was appointed to be organist of the Octagon Chapel in Bath, the fashionable west-country health resort; he entered upon his duties there towards the end of 1767. He was free to supplement his salary with the fees of pupils and the proceeds of concerts; and by 1771 his annual income had risen to nearly four hundred pounds, a considerable sum in those days. His three brothers paid him prolonged visits; and in 1772 he indulged in a Continental tour, visiting Paris and Nancy on his way to Hanover. When he reached home he found his sister Caroline keeping house for her ageing mother and her extravagant brother Jacob. A close bond of affection had always existed between William and his sister, who now, despite efforts at self-education, seemed in danger of settling down as a household drudge. William had already discussed with his brother Alexander the possibility of having her trained as a singer; and when, later in the summer, he returned from Hanover to Bath, he brought Caroline with him to keep house and to be launched upon a musical career. She enjoyed, indeed, a brief springtime of success as a vocalist; but soon the task of helping to train her brother's choir curtailed her own hours of practice, and when, a little later, she followed him into the unfamiliar world of science, her cherished hope of an independent career faded for ever.

Herschel later described his gradual progression from music to astronomy in a letter to the mathematician Charles

c

Hutton: 'The theory of music being connected with mathematics had induced me very early to read in Germany all what had been written upon the subject of harmony; and when not long after my arrival in England the valuable book of Dr Smith's Harmonics came into my hands, I perceived my ignorance and had recourse to other authors for information, by which I was drawn on from one branch of mathematics to another' (*Scientific Papers*, I, xix). Following the study of Robert Smith's *Harmonics*, he passed on to the same author's *Opticks*, which contains an illustrated section on descriptive astronomy; and he was thus stirred to examine the wonders of the heavens for himself with the aid of such instruments as also fell within the wide scope of Smith's manual. Herschel's earliest recorded astronomical observations date from February 1766; they relate to the planet Venus and to an eclipse of the Moon. For nearly ten years yet astronomy remained for him a marginal hobby, to be cultivated only in time spared from his professional duties. In 1774 his diary shows him still giving up to eight music lessons a day, while by night he observes the heavens 'with telescopes of my own construction'; by 1779 he has deliberately reduced the daily number of his scholars to not more than three or four; and in 1782 he records how 'some of them made me give them astronomical instead of musical lessons'.

Herschel's reference to his employment of home-made telescopes foreshadows what was to be one of the most remarkable achievements of his whole career, his fashioning of a multitude of magnificent instruments of higher quality and power than any known before or obtainable elsewhere in his lifetime. Without his unrivalled ingenuity in the design of telescopes and their adjuncts, his patience in the laborious task of constructing them, and his expertise in their use, all his other gifts would scarcely have availed to raise him above the level of a provincial amateur. An outline of his technical procedures must be deferred to a later chapter; but a few passages from Caroline Herschel's memoirs may serve to show how ruthlessly her brother sacrificed leisure, comfort, and the graces of home life to his consuming passion to see further into space than any man before him:

But every leisure moment was eagerly snatched at for resuming some work which was in progress, without taking time for changing dress, and many a lace ruffle was torn or bespattered by molten pitch, etc., besides the danger to which he continually exposed himself by the uncommon precipitancy which accompanied all his actions. . . . For my time was so much taken up with copying music and practising, besides attendance on my brother when polishing, since, by way of keeping him alive, I was constantly obliged to feed him by putting the victuals by bits into his mouth. This was once the case when, in order to finish a seven foot mirror, he had not taken his hands from it for sixteen hours together. In general he was never unemployed at meals, but was always at those times contriving or making drawings of whatever came in his mind. (*Memoir and Correspondence*, 37f.)

Caroline could recall how her brother 'used to retire to bed with a basin of milk or glass of water, and Smith's "Harmonics and Optics," Ferguson's "Astronomy", etc., and so went to sleep buried under his favourite authors' (ibid., 35).

After a few years Herschel grew tired of desultory celestial observations and began to apply himself to one of the outstanding problems which had long perplexed astronomers and to which we have already referred, that of confirming from observations of carefully chosen stars the annual revolution of the Earth about the Sun, and of determining the distances of those stars from us. This quest soon turned into a search for 'double stars', close stellar pairs believed to afford a sensitive test of the Earth's motion. Herschel's earliest explorations of the heavens were phased into three successive 'reviews', marked by a progressive improvement in the power of the instruments employed and by a corresponding extension of scope so as to include fainter and fainter stars.

Herschel's second review was begun in August 1779; and one evening late in December of that year he was observing the Moon with an 8-foot reflector and had found it convenient to set up the instrument in the street in front of his house, which had no garden. A gentleman passing at the time asked permission to look through the telescope: it was granted, and the passer-by proved to be William Watson, son of the more celebrated Dr William Watson, physician and pioneer in electrical experiments. Both were Fellows of the Royal Society and both were later knighted. The younger Watson promptly enrolled Herschel as a member of the short-lived Philosophical Society of Bath, then in process of formation; and it was before that studious company that the astronomer read his earliest scientific papers, to the number of thirty-one in all. They covered a wide range of subjects, some physical ('What becomes of Light?', 'On the Electrical Fluid', etc.) and some metaphysical in the fashion of the time ('On the Existence of Space'). Watson rendered Herschel an important service by communicating to the Royal Society several other papers, of astronomical interest, which the young amateur had presented to the Bath fraternity.

It was, again, in the course of this second review of the heavens, carried out with a reflecting telescope of 7 feet focal length, that Herschel, on 13 March 1781, made a discovery of a kind unprecedented in recorded human history, nothing less than the detection of a major planet of the solar system. This event, which divided the astronomer's life-span into two nearly equal parts, marked the close of his years of struggle and obscurity and the beginning of his career as a national figure in the world of science. For his discovery of the new planet, which in due course received the name of Uranus, the Royal Society in November 1781 awarded Herschel its Copley Medal; and the following month he was elected a Fellow of the Society.

In April 1782 Herschel was informed that King George III had expressed a wish to see him; and, having made out a list of double stars which could be shown to advantage, he packed his 7-foot telescope and travelled to London late in May. He was given hospitality by the elder William Watson, who lived in Lincoln's Inn Fields. A few days later Herschel was graciously received by the King, who directed that the telescope should be sent to Greenwich. There the instrument remained for a month during which the Astronomer Royal and other experts made trial of it and declared that in definition and in magnifying-power it excelled all other telescopes they had ever seen. It was then transported to Windsor where, on 2 July, Herschel showed the planets Jupiter and Saturn and other celestial objects to the King and Queen and their family. With a little prompting from the younger Watson, Herschel was induced to apply to the King for the means of devoting himself wholly to astronomy. It was soon arranged that he should give up his musical profession and settle some-where in the neighbourhood of Windsor, and that he should receive a salary of two hundred pounds a year with only the obligation of occasional attendance upon the Royal Family to show them celestial objects of interest through the telescope. The King subsequently made an allowance of fifty pounds a year to Caroline Herschel as her brother's assistant. And, as we shall see, he authorized substantial grants for the construction and maintenance of the great 40-foot telescope.

So it was that the Herschels forsook the social life of a gay and beautiful city for the inexorable routine of an observatory, geared to the revolving heavens. On 2 August 1782 they moved into their new house at Datchet, about a mile and a half from Windsor Castle; and in the garden the astronomer erected his favourite telescope, a 20-foot reflector (Pl. 6). From now on, for many years, so as not to miss a single hour of possible observing-time, he would watch through the night for a clear spell, or post a work-man to do so; the available hours of daylight he would spend in his workshop. It was during the three years spent at Datchet that Herschel published his earliest papers on two of the principal themes of his lifelong research in astronomy—the free motion through space of the Sun and its planetary family, and the structure of the system of stars of which the Sun is a member. However, the Datchet house suffered from the drawback that the surrounding land was flooded whenever the Thames overflowed its banks; and after suffering a severe attack of ague Herschel removed in June 1785 to Clay Hall in Old Windsor. But the landlady proved a tyrant, and the Herschels departed within a year. They finally settled at Slough in the house on the Windsor Road which stood until recent years as the home of the great astronomer's descendants and the re-pository of his relics. Here Herschel recommenced his ob-servations on 3 April 1786, and here he was to spend the rest of his days.

During his thirty-six years at Slough, Herschel returned to the problems of the solar motion and the structure of the stellar system; other matters that engaged his attention were the theory of telescopic observations, the constitution of the Sun and the physics of the solar radiation, planetary and cometary studies, the phenomena of variable, nebulous, and double stars, the classification of stars according to their brightness, the cataloguing of nebulae and star clusters discovered while 'sweeping' the heavens, and theories of the evolution of celestial systems. It was at

Slough, moreover, that he built the great 40-foot telescope. Papers on these subjects followed one another in no very logical order: we shall try to explain their contents systematically in Chapters 3-5.

As Herschel's fame grew he received an increasing number of requests from astronomers and foreign potentates for telescopes of his fashioning. The sale of telescopes from Herschel's workshop became a lucrative business; hundreds of them were distributed all over Britain and the Continent, realizing thousands of pounds. It may seem a matter for regret that the great astronomer's time and energy should have been taxed in this manner, and to so little purpose. For we do not read of epoch-making discoveries made by the King of Spain or by other recipients of these aids to vision. Perhaps the best such investment was the 7-foot reflector (cf. Pl. 3) sold to Hieronymus Schröter for sixty-five pounds. However, this trade obliged Herschel to maintain a staff of mechanics for carrying out the rough work to which, after all, he had only to give the finishing touches; and it afforded an incentive for 'expensive experiments' (2,160 are recorded) on polishing mirrors by machinery. So that perhaps, on balance, astronomy may have benefited by this diversion.

Herschel was occasionally assisted in his manufacture of telescopes by his brother Alexander. Although not the eldest son William early adopted something of a guardian's role towards his rather unstable brothers Alexander and Dietrich, both brilliant musicians but generally objects of solicitude whenever they flit across the pages of his life story. After his father's death Alexander joined his brother William in England, where he remained for nearly fifty years, passing his time between the orchestras of Bath and the workshop at Slough. In 1816 he broke down in health and joined Dietrich at Hanover, William making provision for him until his death in 1821. Dietrich, the youngest

brother, was of a mercurial, wayward disposition: in 1777
William left a wooden eyepiece unfinished on the lathe
to go in pursuit of him, upon learning that he was running
away to the East Indies. In 1807 Dietrich, broken and
embittered by a further occupation of Hanover, left his
family and came to England to seek a livelihood, remaining
for nearly four years.

In the summer of 1786, soon after he had settled at
Slough, Herschel made what proved to be his final visit to
Germany, taking with him one of his 10-foot reflectors as
a gift from King George III to the University of Göttingen, and seeing his mother for the last time. At her
brother's suggestion Caroline Herschel had taken up
comet-hunting on her own account; and during his two
months' absence in Germany she discovered her first
comet. She was equipped with a small reflecting telescope
having the wide field of view suited to its purpose; her
observing-station was the flat roof of a small detached
building used as a library and as her private apartment,
and later known as the Cottage. Although her own career
as an observer was increasingly sacrificed to her brother's
more illustrious researches, yet between 1786 and 1797
she discovered eight comets in all, as well as many previously uncatalogued nebulae.

Two years after the settlement at Slough, on 8 May
1788, William Herschel married Mrs Mary Pitt (née
Baldwin), widow of John Pitt of Upton, the parish to
which the Herschels belonged. There was one child of the
marriage, John Frederick William, born on 7 March 1792.
The marriage marked a crisis in the dedicated life of
Caroline Herschel. For close upon sixteen years she had
kept house for her brother and, in her devotion to him,
had abandoned a promising musical career to acquire un-
congenial and exacting techniques. Now, at the age of
thirty-eight, she was obliged in the natural order of things

to give place to a stranger. Although she continued as her brother's assistant she felt obliged to remove to rooms in the neighbourhood. Her journals for this period, in which her inmost feelings were recorded, she afterwards destroyed. However, she eventually established friendly relations with her sister-in-law; and she found in her nephew, John Herschel, an object of solicitude during his weakling infancy, later of hope as his genius unfolded, and at last of pride when his scientific achievements, second only to his father's, were acclaimed the world over.

Throughout his career Herschel enjoyed the respect and regard of the leading astronomers of his day, and much of his correspondence with them was carefully preserved in his Letter Book. With a smaller band of his contemporaries he early formed enduring ties of friendship, and particularly with the younger Watson who first made his work known to the Royal Society. Herschel's election to the Society brought him into close touch with its President, Sir Joseph Banks, naturalist and explorer, who had come to occupy a commanding position in British science comparable to that once held by Newton. One of Banks's staunchest supporters was Charles Blagden, an army medical officer and traveller, who became a Secretary of the Society in 1784; it was to him that Caroline wrote in 1786 to report the discovery of her first comet, her brother being in Germany. Other friends were Alexander Aubert, London business man and astronomer, who cordially received the Herschels at his well-equipped private observatory near Deptford, and Patrick Wilson, Professor of Astronomy at Glasgow, who, after his retirement, came with his sister on a visit to Slough and took part in some solar observations there. A highly placed friend and well-wisher of Herschel was the Astronomer Royal, Nevil Maskelyne, from whom he often received timely and precise information as to the whereabouts of newly discovered

celestial objects, and who first guessed the true planetary
status of Uranus. Herschel's foreign correspondents included J. H. Schröter, a lawyer and amateur astronomer of
Bremen, who spent many years studying the surface features of the Moon and planets with a 7-foot reflector of
Herschel's construction, and who has been called the
'Herschel of Germany'. Their friendship was undisturbed
by Herschel's good-natured banter at Schröter's claim to
have observed on the planet Venus mountains more than
six times the height of Chimborazo, but of which the
Slough telescopes revealed no trace. Another correspon-
dent was the distinguished French astronomer Lalande,
who visited Herschel in 1788 and continued to correspond
with him as opportunity offered even after the outbreak
of the Revolutionary War.

Herschel's bride brought him a considerable fortune;
and in his later years he increasingly indulged a taste for
travel as a relief from his round-the-clock scientific activities. In 1792, the year of his son's birth, he made two
extensive tours through England and Scotland in the company of his friend, General John Komarzewski, a cultured
Polish nobleman, who, with William Watson, stood god-
father to the boy. The travellers seem to have concentrated
their attention chiefly upon industrial developments in the
regions through which they passed. At Birmingham they
were the guests of James Watt, the improver of the steam-
engine; and Herschel returned to Slough with his notebooks crammed with sketches of the new machines which
were transforming Britain from an agricultural country
into the workshop of the world. At Glasgow University
the astronomer received the Degree of Doctor of Laws,
and at Edinburgh he made the acquaintance of the chemist
Joseph Black. Again, in the summer of 1802, Herschel,
accompanied by his wife and ten-year-old son, visited
Paris. He met several of the leading French men of science,

among them the astronomers Laplace, Delambre, and Messier, the chemists Berthollet and Fourcroy, and the pioneer balloonist J. A. C. Charles; and he was received by the First Consul, Napoleon Bonaparte. In the winter of 1808 Herschel suffered a severe nervous illness from the effects of which he never completely recovered. To these last years of his life, however, belong some of his boldest searchings into the origin of the stars and their aggregation into clusters and his final attempt to estimate the dimensions of the Galaxy. A tour in the summer of 1809 took the Herschels to the Lake District, and on the way back to Slough they called at Cambridge. Here Mrs Herschel introduced her son to St John's College where he was soon to enter as an undergraduate, living in lodgings with his mother to keep house for him. In 1810 the family journeyed to Scotland, calling once again at Birmingham to see James Watt, and in later years they made further extended tours. In 1813 John Herschel graduated as Senior Wrangler and was proposed by his father for the Fellowship of the Royal Society, though not yet of age. After casting about for a profession he became his father's assistant in 1816.

Herschel was enrolled by many European learned societies, and he was knighted by the Prince Regent in 1816. A long strand of history linking Herschel with the life of astronomy in our own day is constituted by the Royal Astronomical Society, of which in old age he became the first President and in the foundation of which his son John Herschel played a prominent part (see J. L. E. Dreyer and H. H. Turner, *History of the Royal Astronomical Society, 1820-1920*, London, 1923). The Society was constituted at a meeting held on 12 January 1820 at the Freemasons' Tavern in London; the fourteen present included John Herschel together with Francis Baily and William Pearson, who seem to have been the prime movers in the enterprise. A committee was formed and the younger Herschel undertook the preparation of an address explaining the aims of the Society and designed to enlist support for its activities. The Officers and Council of what was at first called the Astronomical Society of London (it received a Royal Charter eleven years later) were elected at a general meeting held on 29 February 1820, Sir William Herschel being appointed a Vice-President and his son Foreign Secretary. In accordance with the practice of many learned academies of the time, a nobleman, the Duke of Somerset, was elected President. However, Herschel's old friend, Sir Joseph Banks, who had been President of the Royal Society for some forty years, now expressed his strong opposition to the formation of the new Society; and he persuaded the Duke of Somerset, who was his close friend, to withdraw from its membership and to decline the Presidency. Banks had previously opposed the establishment of the Geological Society and the Royal Institution. He seems to have feared that the creation of such specialist associations would be the ruin of the Royal Society, which had happily united the interests of the various sciences throughout the century and a half of its existence. The names of various noblemen were canvassed; but at the end of the year, and only upon a second invitation, Sir William Herschel consented to be elected President on the understanding that he should not be expected to take any active part in the work of the Society. Meanwhile, with the death of Banks in the summer of 1820, the Presidency of the Royal Society had passed to Sir Humphry Davy, whose relations with the new astronomical fellowship were more cordial. Herschel indeed never attended any of the Society's meetings, but his last paper, a final instalment of his catalogue of double stars, was published in the first volume of its *Memoirs*.

William Herschel died peacefully at his home in Slough

on 25 August 1822 in his eighty-fourth year. He was buried at Upton in the Church of St Lawrence. A stone tablet under the tower marks the spot and bears a Latin inscription in which occur the words so often quoted in tribute to the great astronomer: *Cœlorum perrupit claustra* (He broke through the barriers of the heavens).

For well over a century the name of William Herschel found no place upon the roll of great British men of science whose fame is celebrated in Westminster Abbey. However, in 1954, through the generosity of the late J. E. Bullard, an inscribed memorial stone was placed in the floor of the Abbey near the tomb of the astronomer's son, Sir John Herschel. The inscription runs:

COELORUM PERRUPIT CLAUSTRA

1738

WILLIAM HERSCHEL

1822

ALIBI SEPULTUS

The tablet was dedicated by the Dean of Westminster on the evening of 8 November 1954, and the reigning President of the Royal Astronomical Society delivered an address (see *The Observatory*, 74 (1954), 243ff.).

After tracing Herschel's life story, reading through his published correspondence, and studying his scientific papers, so full of personal expression and reminiscence, one should be able to form some conception of what manner of man he was. But this is not easy, for his age, though not yet remote in time, is separated from ours by the gulf of an intellectual and social revolution which makes it almost impossible for us to enter into his mental experience or to share in imagination his outlook upon life.

The main watershed dividing the eighteenth from later centuries was the French Revolution. When it began in

1789 Herschel had passed his fiftieth birthday; his charac-
ter was formed and his career was established, and he remained securely rooted in the eighteenth century. Another
world-transforming movement of which Herschel lived
through some of the crucial phases was the Industrial
Revolution. He was conscious only of its exhilarating
aspects as he roved through the Midland factory towns
filling his notebooks with drawings of the exciting new
machines. But we look back at him from an age still con-
vulsed by the consequences of these and of other scarcely
less momentous movements of history. The doctrines of
Marx, whether accepted or rejected, have beclouded our
vision of Herschel as a disinterested investigator who,
single-handed, changed the whole course of the current
of human thought about the Universe, while at a deeper
level the teachings of Freud have sapped the faith of many
in man as a being capable of rational or morally responsible
behaviour. If, in the condition to which modern thought
has reduced us, we are to form any idea of what it felt like
to be William Herschel, it must be through the account
that he gave of himself or that his friends gave of him.

In letters which he wrote in his early twenties to his
brother Jacob, classified as 'musical', 'characteristic'
(humorous), 'moral', and so forth, and penned in English,
French, or German according to their mood, Herschel
dramatizes his lonely life and his innocent romantic encounters in the sentimental fashion of his day. But some
of the letters are marked 'metaphysical', for he shared the
German love of philosophy and always strove to attain
the utmost clarity of thought and expression. Typically
German, too, was the strong bond of affection which
bound the Herschel family together and the attitude of
responsibility for all its members which William was already assuming. Herschel had been schooled by his
German father in a strongly practical cast of piety; and

though in the fashion of the age he exercised his youthful wits upon the philosophical 'proofs' of the existence of God, his mind did not run naturally to speculation on such mysteries. Writing in 1761 on rival theories as to the nature of the soul, he concludes, 'I think it better to remain content with my ignorance till it pleases the Creator of all things to call me to Himself and to draw away the thick curtain which now hangs before our eyes' (*The Herschel Chronicle*, 28).

In his mature years Herschel seems to have adopted a religious position widely shared by educated men of his day and in harmony with the prevailing temper of the Church of England. He believed that the Universe was fashioned by a divine Creator, whose power and wisdom are made more abundantly evident by the scientist, who unveils the operations of nature. He made no concessions to those whose faith was bound up with an almost biblical architecture of the Universe. And he does not seem to have anticipated that his conception of the celestial systems as having reached their present condition through a long, slow process of development might offend some who had been taught to regard the Creation as a sudden event in which the world originated essentially as we know it today. When the Genevan scientist M. A. Pictet, who had visited Herschel at Slough, suggested after the astronomer's death that his views on the condensation of nebulous matter tended to irreligion, John Herschel wished it to be 'distinctly understood that my father, so far from contemplating such consequences, was a sincere believer in, and worshipper of, a benevolent, intelligent and superintending Deity, whose glory he conceived himself to be legitimately forwarding by investigating the magnificent structure of the Universe' (ibid., 197). It was characteristic, also, of the religious tradition to which Herschel adhered that it showed little interest in doctrine beyond the central theistic affirmation of an all-wise and all-powerful Creator; so far as it possessed any specifically Christian content, this was merely ethical or moralistic. In a revealing letter to his son on the choice of a career, Herschel urged the advantages of the Church over the legal profession which John had thought of adopting and which he did in fact pursue for a few months. To his son's objection that the path into the Church was wide and beaten, he replies, 'Such a path must surely lead to happiness, or else it would never be so wide or so beaten'. And he brushes aside his son's intellectual difficulties with the remark that 'the most conscientious clergyman may preach a sermon full of sound morality, and no one will require of him to enter into theological subtilities.' It appeared to Herschel 'the most material circumstance' that a clergyman 'without the least derangement of his ostensible means of livelihood, has time for the attainment of the more elegant branches of literature, for poetry, for music, for drawing, for natural history, for short pleasant excursions of travelling, for being acquainted with the *spirit* of the laws of his country, for history, for political economy, for mathematics, for astronomy, for metaphysics, and for being an author upon any one subject in which his most advantageous and respectable situation has qualified him to excel' (ibid., 349f.). Herschel was not particularly worldly, he was incapable of cynicism, and he was writing with the greatest seriousness to an only son facing the momentous choice of a career. But the days were coming when it would be no longer possible even for an unbeliever to write in such a manner of the ministry of the Churches. And that is a measure of the impact of the great revivals, both the Evangelical and the Catholic, upon the deadness and unspirituality which were the worst faults of the conventional religion, exemplified at its best in such a man as William Herschel.

Plate 3   A 7-foot telescope by Herschel, of Newtonian type.

Plate 4 Herschel's lathe on which he turned the eyepieces of his telescopes.

Plate 5 A selection of Herschel's eyepieces.

We may also learn something of Herschel the man from the first-hand impressions of him which his friends placed on record. These impressions appear to have been consistently agreeable. In 1797, and again in later years, the Herschels were visited at Slough by Dr Charles Burney, father of Fanny Burney the novelist and diarist; he wrote warmly of their happy family life and of the hospitable reception he received: 'Herschel, you know, and every body knows, is one of the most pleasing and well-bred natural characters of the present age, as well as the greatest astronomer' (*Memoirs of Doctor Burney*, by his daughter Madame d'Arblay (London, 1832), iii, 252). And Thomas Campbell the poet, writing in 1813, has left this picture of the astronomer in his old age:

I wish you had been with me the day before yesterday, when you would have joined me, I am sure, deeply, in admiring a great, simple, good old man—Dr. Herschel. . . . Now, for the old Astronomer himself—his simplicity, his kindness, his anecdotes, his readiness to explain, and make perfectly perspicuous too, his own sublime conceptions of the Universe, are indescribably charming. He is seventy-six, but fresh and stout; and there he sat, nearest the door, at his friend's house, alternately smiling at a joke, or contentedly sitting without share or notice in the conversation. Any train of conversation he follows implicitly; anything you ask, he labours with a sort of boyish earnestness to explain. . . . After leaving Herschel, I felt elevated and overcome; and have, in writing to you, made only this memorandum of some of the most interesting moments of my life. T. C. (W. Beattie, *Life and Letters of Thomas Campbell* (London, 1849), ii, 234ff.)

Though he had known war, struggle, and hardship, Herschel suffered singularly little psychological damage from life: he was one of the 'uninjured Minds', in Wordsworth's phrase. His historic achievements in astronomy were securely based upon his technical skill in the design, construction, and use of instruments; these afforded him

D

throughout his career a decisive advantage over everyone else in the world in the pursuit of a whole branch of science. But at the highest creative level he owed most to his capacity for imaginatively organizing the information with which these instruments supplied him, and to the perfect balance which he managed to maintain between the complementary elements of observation and inter-pretation normally present in every scientific investigation. As he wrote in 1785:

> If we indulge a fanciful imagination and build worlds of our own, we must not wonder at our going wide from the path of truth and nature; but these will vanish like the Cartesian vortices, that soon gave way when better theories were offered. On the other hand, if we add observation to observation, without attempting to draw not only certain conclusions, but also con-jectural views from them, we offend against the very end for which only observations ought to be made. I will endeavour to keep a proper medium; but if I should deviate from that, I could wish not to fall into the latter error.

After her brother's death Caroline Herschel returned to spend the last twenty-five years of her life at Hanover. At first she made her home with her only surviving brother Dietrich; when he died a few years later she removed to lodgings. Her old age was cheered by the friendship of a Madame Beckedorff whom she had known when they both were girl pupils in a dressmaking-school, and again later at Windsor, where her friend was one of the ladies of Queen Charlotte's household. In the early days of her retirement she made one more great effort for astronomy and for her brother's memory. She compiled a catalogue of the 2,500 nebulae and star clusters which he had dis-covered, classifying them into zones of increasing distance from the pole and computing their positions for the year 1800. She sent the completed catalogue to her nephew John Herschel, then engaged upon a review of these objects; and he later acknowledged the great value it had been to him in his work. For this last contribution, though it remained unpublished, she was in 1828 awarded the Gold Medal of the Astronomical Society. In 1846 she learned of the discovery of the planet later called Neptune, the existence and position of which were established by the analysis of the disturbances which it produced in the motion of her brother's planet, Uranus.

Caroline Herschel died on 9 January 1848 in her ninety-eighth year and was buried in the Gartenkirchhof in Hanover.

William Herschel's life-work was completed, in the most literal sense, by his son John, who, having re-examined the known nebulae and double stars of the northern heavens (and added appreciably to their number), extended his survey to embrace the southern celestial hemisphere. Establishing himself at the Cape of Good Hope with his family and instruments, he remained there for four years (1834-8), sweeping and gauging the regions of the sky invisible from Slough. He also carried out experiments on the brightness of stars, which helped to lay the foundation for the exact definition of stellar magnitudes in force today; and he followed up his father's studies in solar physics by linking the formation of sunspots with the rotation of the Sun, and by measuring, with homely apparatus, the intensity of the solar radiation. And to the end of his long and arduous life (he died in 1871) he was largely occupied with setting in order and publishing the results of his own and his father's labours.

Chapter 3

Herschel's Contributions to Astronomy—1

We have traced Herschel's life story and have referred in general terms to the problems which engaged his attention from time to time. We shall now try to explain his researches in astronomy in greater detail and in a more systematic manner. Herschel's scientific career cannot conveniently be broken up, as Newton's can, into successive periods each marked by some consuming preoccupation. From the beginning his interest flowed along several different lines of investigation which he pursued concurrently, combining them where possible or switching from one to another; and to discuss his contributions in the order of their publication would only create confusion. Instead we shall group his papers according to subject; and it would seem appropriate to begin with some account of his telescopes and next to consider his discoveries and speculations concerning our nearest celestial neighbours of the solar system, passing thence to his pioneer studies on the stars both as physical objects and as an organized and developing community.

1 Herschel's Telescopes

It was in 1773, during the period of his residence at Bath, that William Herschel began to make telescopes. At first he constructed refractors, using ready-made lenses; but the high cost of the latter, and the cumbrousness of the long tubes required, soon induced him to turn to reflectors, for which metal mirrors of large diameter, or aperture, could be cast and polished even by an amateur.

Isaac Newton constructed the earliest reflecting telescope about 1668. He solved as best he could the problem of fashioning a small concave mirror; but during the eighteenth century the technique was improved, notably by the astronomers John Hadley and Samuel Molyneux. Their methods were described by Robert Smith in his *Compleat System of Opticks* (Cambridge, 1738, ii, 301 ff.). This book embodies a history of telescopic astronomy up to the time when it was written; and it furnishes a detailed account of the contemporary technique of grinding and polishing lenses and specula and of building them into telescopes and other optical instruments. The procedure described for making a telescopic speculum was broadly as follows. Circular brass gauges were first cut to the curvature prescribed for the speculum. These were employed in turning to a true figure a pewter pattern which, in its turn, served to shape a mould of sand into which the molten speculum metal was poured. There followed the laborious process of grinding and polishing the casting till it received the precise spherical or paraboloidal figure intended. Various procedures were currently recommended for converting the rough casting into a perfect mirror. This process involved the use of an accurately shaped 'tool', the choice of suitable abrasive and polishing materials, and the adoption of an effective 'polishing-stroke' by which the tool was applied to the casting in a to-and-fro motion along its various diameters, or in circular sweeps round its centre, or in some other manner.

The study of Smith's *Opticks* had helped to inspire Herschel with a keen desire to examine the wonders of the heavens for himself, and the book now became his guide to telescope-making. He also received some hints from an amateur living at Bath who had tired of the hobby and who willingly sold his stock of optical tools and half-finished mirrors to the young enthusiast. Makers of reflecting telescopes had always been faced with the problem of deciding upon the composition of the metallic alloy of which the speculum was to be made. The polished surface must be brilliantly reflecting, non-porous, and slow to tarnish; and the metal should be easy to work, not too brittle, nor too sensitive to changes of temperature which might distort the shape of the speculum. Copper, silver, tin, antimony, and arsenic, in various proportions, were all favoured. At one time Herschel was led by his experiments to believe that five pounds of tin to twelve pounds of copper gave the best results. It was his practice to cast his specula in moulds of loam baked by burning charcoal; in one instance the mould was made of pounded horse-dung. A mould of loam was employed in 1781 for casting a 3-foot speculum which was to have a focal length of 30 feet. The metal was heated in a furnace built in a basement room in Herschel's house. At the first attempt the mould cracked and the molten metal ran out; at the second the fiery stream flowed from the furnace over the paving-stones, some of which cracked and blew up, to the peril of the operators. Herschel used to finish off the castings with brass tools in which 'gutters' (or grooves) of various configurations had been cut; the polishing was done with metal bases covered with pitch and working through a layer of 'crocus' (calcined metal) moistened with water. He experimented with various polishing-strokes but would lay down no general instructions, as each speculum seemed to call for individual treatment best decided by the operator's instinct and experience. In the course of his career Herschel made many telescopes, not only for his own use but also for private purchasers at home and abroad. He ground at least four hundred specula, some of them of large dimensions; and he was compelled to devise machinery for lightening the tedious labour (cf. Pl. 9). To the fashioning of these instruments and the figuring of the mirrors he brought a manual skill and a delicacy of touch which he was wont to attribute to his early training as a violinist. He was somewhat reticent about the technical details of his optical work, which were, in fact, the trade secrets of his increasingly lucrative traffic in telescopes. But he left in manuscript at his death four volumes of notes on 'Experiments on the construction of specula', together with a treatise on mirror-making. These were examined in 1924 by the astronomer Dr W. H. Steavenson, who also described and catalogued the instruments of Herschel's still preserved in that year at the old home at Slough, but since dispersed upon its demolition (*Trans. of the Optical Society*, 26 (1924-5), 210ff.; *Monthly Notices of the Royal Astronomical Society*, 119 (1959), 449ff.).

(*i*) *The Forty-foot Telescope*   Herschel regarded his early experiments on casting and polishing mirrors as a preparation for a much more ambitious enterprise; and towards the end of 1785 he embarked upon the construction of a giant reflecting telescope with a focal length of 40 feet. The expense would have been prohibitive; but the President of the Royal Society, Sir Joseph Banks, brought the project to the notice of King George III who financed it with grants eventually amounting to four thousand pounds. When the instrument came into use the King allowed Herschel an additional two hundred pounds a year for its upkeep.

In 1795 Herschel gave the Royal Society a detailed account of the great instrument (*Phil. Trans.* (1795), 347ff.). It consisted essentially of a sheet-iron tube nearly 40 feet in length, to the lower end of which was secured a metal speculum 4 feet in diameter (Pls. 7, 8, 10). This tube was mounted in a well-knit wooden framework designed to enable the telescope to be directed towards any part of the heavens selected for observation. The whole structure was pivoted centrally upon a stout upright post, and its base rode upon twenty rollers running along low circular walls of masonry. Pivoted at its lower end, the tube could be set by means of pulleys to any desired elevation above the horizon; while the vertical plane of this elevation could be altered by swinging the whole structure round. The telescope was also permitted a sideways motion amounting to a few degrees either way.

Herschel modified the traditional design of reflecting telescopes by attaching the eyepiece to the side of the tube at its open end and tilting the speculum slightly so that it reflected the incident light directly into the eyepiece. He thus avoided the loss of light caused by the reflection which takes place at the secondary mirror in a Newtonian or Gregorian instrument; and this advantage was held to outweigh the drawback that some of the incoming light was obstructed by the interposition of the observer's head. He had tried this so-called 'front view' experimentally as early as 1776 and again in 1783; and he adopted it generally for reflectors of wide aperture. The term 'Herschelian' came to be applied to instruments constructed in this fashion (Fig. 6). For the convenience of the observer working with the 40-foot telescope, a flight of stairs led to a gallery facing the tube, and a ladder afforded access thence to an observing-platform with a seat. Both structures were adjustable to the situation of the telescope. A speaking-tube enabled the observer to communicate with the workman who controlled the movements of the instrument, and with the amanuensis, usually Caroline Herschel, who, equipped with a catalogue, a clock, and an indicator showing the setting of the tube, recorded the observations to her brother's dictation. These assistants were housed in the sheds shown at the base of the instrument.

Herschel's account of his 40-foot telescope affords the reader no information as to the composition of the metallic speculum or the method adopted for grinding and polishing it. These technical details, carefully recorded by the astronomer, were to become known only after his death. It appears that when the speculum had been cast it was

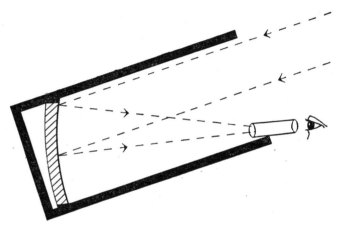

Fig. 6 The 'Herschelian' or 'Front View' type of reflecting telescope.

lowered by means of a crane face downwards on to a convex, pitch-coated 'tool', dusted with moist rouge, upon which it was ground for months by a team of ten men. Herschel in fact prepared *two* specula for alternative use. The first was accidentally made too thin, and the second was almost always used in preference. For many years all trace of the first was lost; but in 1927 it was discovered by Dr Steavenson in a cavity under the stairs of the Cottage, which stood in the grounds of Observatory House, Herschel's old home at Slough, and which served Caroline Herschel as an observing-station (*The Observatory*, 50 (1927), 114ff.). The two specula are now on exhibition in London, the first at the Science Museum, South Kensington, and the second at the National Maritime Museum at Greenwich (see Pl. 10).

The construction of the 40-foot preoccupied Herschel and taxed the energies of his team of workmen for nearly four years. He celebrated its completion on 28 August 1789 when, directing it towards Saturn, he discovered a sixth satellite of the ringed planet. However, the great instrument never quite fulfilled its promise or repaid the wealth and labour that had been lavished upon its construction. It was slow and cumbrous to operate; there were few nights when the atmospheric conditions were such as to justify its use, and Herschel made it a rule never to employ a larger instrument than was necessary for the task in hand. Changes of temperature were apt to cause a layer of vapour or in cold weather of ice, to form upon the mirror, which also tarnished rapidly, requiring to be repolished about every two years. The mirror also suffered some distortion under the stress of its weight of nearly a ton; and the composition of the metal for such a large reflector could not be selected on purely optical considerations. Perhaps too, the instrument, primarily intended for resolving nebulae into star clusters, became somewhat redundant when, a year or so after its completion, Herschel recognized that many intractable nebulae are in fact gaseous and therefore, by their very nature, irresolvable. So it came about that already during Herschel's lifetime the 40-foot reflector was abandoned to decay; and in 1839, seventeen years after his death, it was dismantled to the accompaniment of a requiem specially composed by the astronomer's son and sung by the family, assembled in the great tube. The historic instrument survives today in effigy to adorn the seal of the Royal Astronomical Society; it bears the legend *Quicquid nitet notandum* (Whatever shines must be noted down).

Long experience with reflecting telescopes taught Herschel to recognize the conditions under which these instruments would often behave in a disappointing manner (*Phil. Trans.* (1803), 217ff.). Moisture in the atmosphere was no enemy to excellent vision, even when condensation on the tube was 'running down in streams'; nor was fog prejudicial so long as the stars remained at all visible. Frost, especially when setting in or thawing, often made the stars appear tremulous; wind seemed to increase their apparent diameters; fine, dry weather was often unfavourable to observation. In general the best results were obtained when the mirror and the surrounding atmosphere had reached a uniform temperature and the air was moist. Herschel also noticed, and experimented upon, the effect of the Sun's heating-rays in distorting the figure and altering the focal length of a speculum upon the reflecting-surface of which they fell.

(*ii*) *Space-penetrating power*   Herschel formulated the connection between the aperture of a telescope and the greatest distance through which the instrument enables an observer to see into space. He was fascinated, as we shall see, by the problem of determining the 'construction of the heavens', the shape and size of the great system of stars of which the Sun is a member. But before he could survey and set limits to this vast assemblage of luminaries he had to provide himself with the means of seeing to its utmost bounds. It thus became of practical importance to him to understand what it is that determines the range of a telescope. This range can be thought of as the greatest distance at which a star of standard brightness in itself can just be seen through that instrument under given circumstances.

Herschel distinguished clearly between what he called the *intrinsic* and the *absolute* brightness of an object. If we regard the surface of the object as divided up into small, equal areas, then the average of the quantities of light sent to us from these several surface elements determines the intrinsic brightness of the object, and the total of all these quantities determines the absolute brightness. The intrinsic or surface brightness comes into consideration when one is observing an extended bright surface such as that of the Moon; this brightness does not depend upon the distance of the object. A star on the other hand gives a point image; and whether this is visible or not depends upon the absolute brightness of the image. If the star's distance from the observer could be varied, its apparent brightness would be found to vary inversely as the square of that distance: this was known in Herschel's time. That is to say, multiplying the distance by 2, 3, 4, etc. would reduce the star's apparent brightness to one-quarter, one-ninth, one-sixteenth, etc. of what it was.

In a paper read to the Royal Society in November 1799, Herschel discussed what he called the 'space-penetrating power' of a telescope, with a view to constructing instruments capable of plumbing the ocean of stars to its depths (*Phil. Trans.* (1800), 49ff.). And he showed that this property depended upon and was, broadly speaking, proportional to the *aperture* of the telescope, that is, to the diameter of its object glass or speculum. For suppose a telescope to be just powerful enough to enable an observer looking through it to see some faint star. If this star could now be removed to *twice* its distance from us it would no longer be visible through that telescope, for the intensity of the light reaching us would be only *one-quarter* of what it was. But a second telescope differing from the first only in having an object glass or mirror of *twice* the diameter (and therefore *four times* the area) would collect four times as much of this fainter light and thus just compensate for the diminution of its intensity;

and the star would again be just visible to the observer. Similarly, a telescope with three times the aperture would bring the star into view at three times the distance and so on, neglecting losses by scattering and absorption suffered by the light in passing through the instrument, losses which Herschel sought to estimate experimentally.

Herschel distinguished clearly between the space-penetrating-power of a telescope and its magnifying-power. He also discovered that his capacity to distinguish close pairs or clusters of stars as separate points of light—to *resolve* them, as we should say—depended not only upon the magnifying-power of his eyepiece but also upon the aperture of his object glass: the greater the aperture the greater the resolving-power. He found that penetrating-power and magnification militated against each other beyond a certain point: 'In the use of either power, the injudicious overcharge of the other will prove hurtful to perfect vision'. And he suggested that there was a limit beyond which attempts to penetrate farther into space were not profitable, any more objects brought into view being outshone by the general light of the heavens. Herschel also grasped the principle (of great relevance to the cosmological speculation of our own day) that light reaching us from the depths of space reveals the local conditions obtaining at its place of origin at the time when it set out on its long journey: 'A telescope with a power of penetrating into space, . . . has also, as it may be called, a power of penetrating into time past' (*Phil. Trans.* (1802), 498).

2 *The Mountains of the Moon*

One of Herschel's earliest papers, read to the Bath Society and subsequently communicated by Watson to the Royal Society (*Phil. Trans.* (1780), 507), described his attempts to estimate the heights of the lunar mountains. Observing the Moon through his newly invented telescope in 1609, Galileo had discovered that our satellite was not the 'perfect' sphere which a heavenly body was traditionally supposed to be, but that its surface was diversified with mountains and valleys such as we find upon the Earth. Galileo ingeniously attempted to determine by observation the heights of certain of the lunar mountains; and he was followed in this enterprise by later astronomers.

Herschel resolved to repeat these observations with greater accuracy, using a Newtonian reflector and a bifilar micrometer (see p. 8). Recasting the classic procedure, he would select a lunar peak just visible as an isolated point of light rising above the shaded portion of the Moon's surface and would then measure its angular distance from the boundary of the illuminated part. The result enabled him to calculate the height of the peak in terms of the known radius of the Moon and thence in miles. His observations seemed to suggest that the heights of lunar mountains had been exaggerated by earlier observers, who had assigned to them values of up to five miles. Herschel believed that most of them did not exceed half a mile in altitude; modern observers estimate the heights of the highest peaks at up to 20,000 feet. Herschel occasionally employed alternative methods of estimating the heights of lunar mountains. He would measure the lengths of the shadows they cast on the Moon's surface, or how far they projected from the Moon's disc.

The study which Herschel made of the Moon's surface created in him at this early period of his life a conviction of 'the great probability, not to say almost absolute certainty, of her being inhabited'. And quoting his 'real sentiments' in a letter to Maskelyne, the Astronomer Royal, about this paper, he declared, 'Were I to chuse between the Earth and Moon I should not hesitate a moment to fix upon the Moon for my habitation.' Again, in 1794, Herschel expressed his conviction that the Moon is stocked with inhabitants suited to the conditions prevailing there, which are scarcely more extreme than those to which life adapts itself on the Earth.

On several occasions Herschel was convinced that he could see active volcanoes on the Moon; once in 1783, when the appearance of a red, luminous spot on a dark portion of the lunar surface was confirmed by friends viewing it through his instrument, and again four years later when he made his observations the subject of a short report to the Royal Society (*Phil. Trans.* (1787), 229). During a total eclipse of the Moon in 1790 he noticed upon its surface at least a hundred and fifty 'bright, red, luminous points'; but he would not 'venture at a surmise of the cause'. He does not appear to have pursued the matter in his more mature years; and though such claims are still made from time to time they are treated with great reserve by responsible astronomers.

3 *The Constitution of the Sun*

It was Herschel's ultimate aim to extend the scope of astronomy to the remotest stars, far beyond the limits of the Sun's domain; but this only increased his scientific interest in the Sun itself. For he regarded it as a typical star conveniently situated for study at close quarters. The Sun had been recognized from remotest ages as the resplendent source of light and life on the Earth; and Newton had pronounced it the seat of the forces retaining the planets in their orbits. The Sun's distance from the Earth, a quantity of great importance in astronomy, had been determined in Herschel's youth, with an accuracy not previously attained, through observations of the planet Venus in transit across the solar disc. But the investigation of the Sun as a physical object may be said to go back to the early seventeenth century when Galileo and other pioneers of telescopic astronomy first systematically observed the sunspots. The situation of the spots *in* the luminous surface, and their motions from day to day, established that the Sun is slowly rotating and enabled the axis of this rotation and its period, about twenty-five days, to be determined (cf. Pl. 12).

Herschel wanted to unravel the mystery of the Sun's 'internal construction'. The sunspots appeared to offer the most hopeful clue; and already several conflicting views as to their nature had been put forward. Alexander Wilson, Professor of Astronomy at Glasgow, had been led by his observations to regard a sunspot as a depression in the Sun's surface revealing a non-luminous layer below; the shaded border, or penumbra, of the spot represented the shelving sides of the depression (*Phil. Trans.* (1774), 1ff.). He conceived the Sun as a solid, dark sphere encompassed by a thin, luminous covering; a spot was a rift in this envelope caused by the generation of some gas within. On the other hand the French astronomer Lalande, writing two years later, explained the spots as rock-like projections from a solid core alternately exposed and submerged by the ebb and flow of the fiery liquid surrounding the Sun, the penumbra representing the surrounding shallows (*Mém. de l'Acad. R. des Sci.* (1776), 457ff.).

In his first paper on the solar constitution, read in 1794, Herschel too adduced observational evidence to support the view that the Sun was a dark body surrounded by an extensive atmosphere; this was composed of several 'elastic fluids' (gases), one of them luminous and the rest transparent (*Phil. Trans.* (1795), 46ff.). The luminous fluid might be generated by the decomposition of gases somewhat as (he supposed) clouds are formed in our atmosphere; or it could correspond to our aurora borealis. Spots he conceived as rifts in the bright envelope through

Plate 6 Herschel's 20-foot telescope.

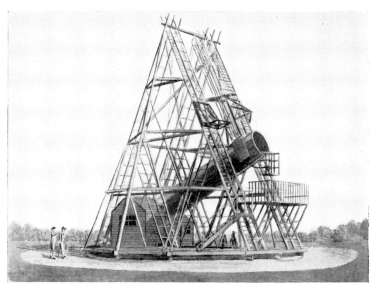

Plate 7 Herschel's 40-foot telescope.

Plate 8   10-foot section from the reflector end of Herschel's 40-foot telescope
(preserved at the National Maritime Museum).

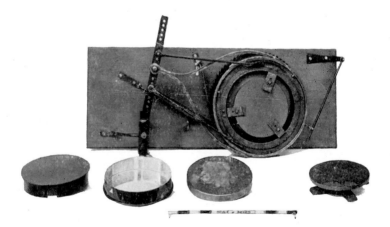

Plate 9   Herschel's polishing machine and brass mount used in
polishing specula.

which we could see the dark surface of the Sun just as an observer on the Moon would see the Earth's surface through gaps in the clouds of our atmosphere. The bright patches, or faculae, apparently elevated above the mottled surface of the Sun were to be regarded as local accumulations of the luminous material. The wastage of the Sun's light might perhaps be made good by the diversion into the Sun of some of the numerous comets, which appeared to consist merely of luminous vapours.

There seemed then, after all, no great dissimilarity between the Sun, 'a very eminent, large, and lucid planet', and the other members of the solar system. Its surface is 'diversified with mountains and vallies'; and 'we need not hesitate to admit that the Sun is richly stored with inhabitants'. To suppose otherwise would be to make the same mistake as Moon-dwellers (Herschel, as we have seen, believed in them also), who should regard the Earth as existing merely to provide them with reflected light when direct sunlight was not to be had. To the objection that the Sun-dwellers would be consumed by the solar heat, endured at such close quarters, Herschel replied that the Sun's rays produce heat only when they enter an appropriate medium such as the Earth's atmosphere. Sounder ideas on the nature of heat were later to render this surmise untenable, though the hypothesis of a 'cold Sun' still persists in unorthodox astronomical circles.

Herschel was writing much in the spirit of eighteenth-century thought when he assumed that Providence had stocked every corner of the Universe with some appropriate form of life. In the same vein he extends the attribute of habitability from the Sun to the stars, arguing that in close star clusters there may be no room for trains of planets, so that if the member stars are to support life it can only be by being themselves inhabited.

Herschel's views on the nature of the Sun show a further

E

development in his paper of 1801 (*Phil. Trans.* (1801), 265ff.). He had undertaken meanwhile a careful study of the Sun's behaviour, hoping to discover any visible causes that might determine variations in its output of light and heat and thus serve for forecasting good or bad harvests. His observations were shared for a time by Patrick Wilson who, after succeeding his father, Alexander Wilson, in the Glasgow Chair of Astronomy, had retired and settled in London and was now on a visit to Slough. It seems that in 1796 he had reproached Herschel for not acknowledging the elder Wilson's priority in establishing the nature of sunspots; but he was satisfied by the astronomer's explanation and the two were now good friends.

In explaining his results Herschel forsakes the traditional names of the principal solar features for a more matter-of-fact terminology of his own which, however, has not been retained. He distinguishes 'openings' (spots or nuclei) where the luminous covering of the Sun is removed and (as he supposed) we look into the dark interior. A large 'opening' is generally bordered by a depressed and faintly luminous 'shallow' (penumbra) and is associated with apparently elevated 'ridges' and 'nodules' of brightly luminous matter (faculae and luculi in the older terminology). The Sun's surface is 'corrugated' into a fleeting pattern of brighter and darker granules which give the impression of being higher and lower respectively than the general surface level. The 'indentations', or depressed parts of the corrugations, may have central dark holes or 'pores'.

Out of his study of all these appearances in their ceaseless transformations there arose in Herschel's mind a picture of the Sun as a solid sphere surrounded by an invisible gaseous atmosphere which extends well beyond the limits of the luminous surface and which is more compressed than the Earth's atmosphere in consequence of the Sun's greater mass and attractive power. In this atmosphere, at the respective heights decided by their relative densities, there float two layers of clouds. The lower clouds are dark, opaque, and probably not unlike those of our atmosphere; and they normally form a continuous screen. The clouds constituting the upper layer are luminous; they are not continuous but form a kind of lattice through the gaps in which we can see small patches of the lower cloud layer, noticeably darker because shining by reflected light, and affording by contrast the impression of a mottled surface. From the depths of the Sun's atmosphere there float up the gases which, by their decomposition, generate the fiery clouds, the bright granules of the corrugations. These gases normally make their ascent through the 'pores' in the lower cloud layer; but when exceptionally abundant they create for themselves the larger 'openings' and force some of the surrounding bright clouds aside, so forming 'shallows'—appearances produced by the light reflected from the lower cloud layer. Fiery vapours are heaped up round the 'openings' to constitute 'ridges' and 'nodules'. The inner layer of cloud serves to shield any inhabitants of the Sun's solid surface from direct exposure to the intolerable radiance, while at the same time, being highly reflective (as was established by a photometric experiment), it increases the Sun's splendour to outward view.

In concluding his paper Herschel listed the observable conditions on the Sun which might be expected to accompany a more or a less than usually abundant emission of solar heat and light, if such fluctuations do in fact occur. And to test whether they do he compared past records of the frequency or absence of sunspots at various times since 1650 with fluctuations in the price of wheat over the same periods, with no very conclusive results. There seemed some reason to suspect that the greatest output of solar heat (and the lowest prices) occurred at times of greater frequency of sunspots, and the least emission at times when the Sun's surface was unbroken and quiescent. This view was revived later in the nineteenth century when the Sun had come to be regarded as belonging to the class of stars which periodically vary in brightness. Its assigned period of variability was that of the eleven-year cycle governing the frequency of sunspots, which Herschel indeed must have come near discovering, but which was first pointed out by Heinrich Schwabe in 1843. In his earlier paper Herschel had suggested that the Sun should be classed with the variable stars. As a rotating, spotted globe it would not present a disc of unvarying brightness to a distant observer: perhaps one half of the Sun consistently emitted less heat and light than the other. Or perhaps incessant changes in the Sun's spot-density must make of it an *irregular* variable star of a type Herschel had already encountered in the heavens. Modern observations, however, do not support the view that the intensity of the Sun's radiation is affected by the sunspot cycle or by any other physical periodicity.

Herschel, then, extended our knowledge of solar phenomena almost to the limit of what was possible with his equipment; and his theory of the Sun's constitution, though rendered untenable by the subsequent progress of physics, yet succeeded for the time being in co-ordinating all the facts it was designed to cover.

4 *The Physics of Solar Radiation*

In observing the Sun with his telescopes Herschel was obliged to protect his eyes with coloured glass shades. In the course of his experiments to discover the most satisfactory type of shade he noticed that the sensation of heat seemed to have little relation to the intensity of the accompanying light but that it varied according to the colour of the glass. He wondered if the variously coloured rays into which a prism breaks up a beam of sunlight might not differ in their powers of heating a surface upon which they fell, and whether the power of illuminating objects might not also be unequally distributed among such rays (*Phil. Trans.* (1800), 255ff.).

To investigate the first of these possibilities Herschel formed a spectrum of sunlight upon a pasteboard screen having in it a slot through which a narrow section of the spectrum, in some selected colour, could fall upon the bulb of a thermometer below (Pl. 14). After a few minutes' exposure to the rays, the reading on the scale of this instrument was compared with that of a second thermometer close to the first but shaded by the screen; and the difference in the readings was taken to indicate the heating-power of the incident rays. This was done for red, green, and violet light, the average heating-effects being found roughly proportional to 55, 24, and 16 respectively. Herschel used in fact three thermometers with blackened bulbs; two of them had been lent to him by Patrick Wilson.

To compare next the illuminating-powers of various coloured lights, Herschel examined through a microscope opaque objects under light from various parts of the spectrum; and he concluded that, in relation to the human eye, 'the maximum of illumination lies in the brightest yellow, or palest green'. Objects appeared equally distinct by whatever spectral colour they were illuminated, and much more distinct than when ordinary light was used. 'May not the chemical properties of the prismatic colours be as different as those which relate to light and heat'? asked Herschel, anticipating what the photographers of the future would not be slow to learn.

Herschel suspected that the heating-effect, increasing

towards the red, did not cease where the visible spectrum reached its limit but continued well into the space beyond: 'the full red falls still short of the maximum of heat; which perhaps lies even a little beyond visible refraction. In this case, radiant heat will at least partly, if not chiefly, consist, if I may be permitted the expression, of invisible light' (ibid., 272). A month later he described how he had confirmed this view by an experiment shown in Plate 15 (*Phil. Trans.* (1800), 284ff.). The illuminated prism cast upon the table a solar spectrum to the red end of which Herschel brought up a stand, covered with ruled paper and supporting his three thermometers. One of these was exposed at various measured distances beyond the visible limit of the spectrum; the others were placed in line with the first but some way to the side. The exposed thermometer showed an excess of temperature over the others. There were therefore heating-rays in the region beyond the visible red, the maximum of heating-power in Herschel's experiment being apparently located about half an inch beyond the spectral limit. Herschel employed his thermometers in a similar exploration beyond the violet end of the visible spectrum, but he could find no evidence of radiant heat in that region. However, in 1801, the year after Herschel's paper appeared, J. W. Ritter demonstrated the existence of invisible rays beyond the violet end of the spectrum through their chemical property of blackening silver chloride.

Herschel's experiments served to establish that radiant heat, like light, suffers refraction in various degrees (the prism acts dispersively upon it); and he went on to prove experimentally that heating-rays, whether solar or terrestrial in origin, whether falling into the visible spectrum or beyond it, follow the same laws of reflection and refraction as do rays of light (*Phil. Trans.* (1800), 293ff., 437ff.). In the earlier stages of his investigation Herschel maintained the view that light and radiant heat were essentially identical; but a long course of experiments on the absorption of heat and light by transparent media shook him in this belief. In the eighteenth century it was generally believed that light and heat consisted of material particles; and it seemed reasonable to suppose that these corpuscles might be of two different kinds as they affected different senses. Many years were to elapse before the heating, lighting, and chemical roles of radiation could be theoretically co-ordinated in a single theory.

To return for a moment to Herschel's original problem of protecting his eyes in solar observations: he would often view the Sun through an eyepiece containing a square metal box having two of its opposite sides made of glass; this was filled with some suitable liquid serving to temper the intensity of the rays as they passed through it (*Phil. Trans.* (1801), 354ff.). Ink diluted with water gave an image of the Sun 'as white as snow'.

A later excursion by Herschel into the realm of pure physics was less auspicious. He devoted three considerable papers (1807-10) to describing and interpreting the optical phenomenon familiar to physics students under the name of Newton's Rings. Already in 1801 Thomas Young had explained the rings as due to interference between light waves. Herschel ignored Young's views, perhaps influenced by Lord Brougham's onslaught upon them. But the wave theory of light soon established itself, and Herschel's speculations in this field were forgotten.

Herschel, however, may be claimed as one of the pioneers of spectroscopic astronomy. In 1798 he attached a prism to the eyepiece of one of his telescopes and observed the colours into which it resolved the light of six stars of the first magnitude, noting the preponderance of red in the star Betelgeuse, of blue in Procyon, and of orange in Arcturus (*Phil. Trans.* (1814), 264).

5 *Planets and Comets*

The ancient astronomers set apart in a class by themselves the Sun, the Moon, and the five bodies to which, following the Romans, we give the names of Mercury, Venus, Mars, Jupiter, and Saturn. They called them the seven planets, or 'wandering stars', because they did not remain fixed in the sky like other stars but pursued winding courses among the constellations as they revolved—about the Earth, it was supposed. Following the Copernican revolution in astronomy, the Sun was recognized as the centre of the planetary system, the Earth as one of the planets, and the Moon as a satellite of the Earth; so that when Herschel was young, six planets were known, to which he soon added a seventh, the Georgian planet, or Uranus. During the eighteenth century much labour was bestowed upon applying Newtonian mechanics to account for the intricate movements of the Moon and planets under the attraction of the Sun and of one another; but Herschel was not a mathematician and he concerned himself rather with studying the physical constitution of these members of the solar system. He thus continued in a tradition begun by the telescopic observers of the seventeenth century, who had turned their instruments upon the planets to map their surface features, to discover their satellites, if any, and to estimate their periods of rotation where possible.

Besides the planets there are the comets, which constitute a sort of second family of the Sun. Down to the seventeenth century they were regarded as entirely capricious in their behaviour, originating from the explosion of vapours in our atmosphere or pursuing unpredictable courses through space. Then Newton and Halley showed that the comets are, at least while visible to us, members of the solar system controlled by the Sun's attraction and following orbits of the same class as those of the planets;

and certain comets, travelling in elongated ellipses about the Sun, are found to return at regular intervals to our skies. Herschel was favoured with opportunities for examining an instructive selection of these awe-inspiring objects; and despite inevitable limitations upon his understanding of the physical processes (still mysterious) which occur when a comet is excited by the Sun's radiation, his observations and theories in this branch of astronomy were remarkably to the point.

We shall now describe Herschel's work on the planets in the order of their increasing distance from the Sun, passing on then to summarize his cometary studies.

(*i*) *A Transit of Mercury*   The planets Mercury and Venus revolve round the Sun in orbits interior to that of the Earth; and from time to time one or other of them passes directly between us and the Sun and can be seen for

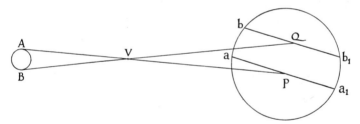

Fig. 7 Observers A and B, stationed in widely different latitudes on the Earth, observe the planet V (Venus or Mercury) trace out apparent paths aa_1, bb_1 across the solar disc. From a knowledge of the times taken for the planet to describe these two paths, conclusions can be drawn leading to an estimate of the Sun's distance from the Earth in terms of the radius of the latter.

a few hours in silhouette as a dark spot passing across the solar disc. Such 'transits' (particularly those of Venus) afford an indirect means of determining the distance of the Sun from the Earth: it is only necessary to record, in various latitudes, the instants when the planet makes and breaks contact with the disc (see Fig. 7).

Herschel observed a transit of Mercury in 1802; he set himself merely to follow the course of events, undistracted by clock-watching (*Phil. Trans.* (1803), 214ff.). The planet's disc appeared sharply outlined and exactly circular, and darker in hue than the sunspots near which it seemed to pass. There was no trace of a bright aureole surrounding the planet such as Schröter and other observers claimed to have noticed during transits of the planet and which was mistakenly believed to indicate a Mercurial atmosphere; nor was there any distortion when the planet crossed the edge of the Sun's disc.

(*ii*) *Venus, the cloud-wrapped planet*   Herschel kept the planet Venus under observation during many years (*Phil. Trans.* (1793), 201ff.). He was anxious to discover whether it was rotating on an axis like the Earth, and if so, what was its period of rotation—its 'day'—which had been variously estimated by astronomers. The obvious procedure was to select some mark upon the planet's surface and to measure the time required for it to be carried right round the planet and back to its starting-point. This would fix the period approximately; a comparison of observations of the planet made at widely separated times would then serve to determine it with great precision. Despite occasional impressions of transient markings on Venus, Herschel was soon forced to conclude that the planet was enveloped in a densely cloud-laden atmosphere hiding its surface features so completely as to make determinations of the axis and period of rotation impossible. And this is still the situation today; although spectroscopic techniques not available in Herschel's time suggest that the period cannot be less than about ten days. Finally Herschel estimated the size of Venus, making it about equal to the Earth, or a little larger: in actual fact its diameter is about a hundred miles less than that of the Earth.

(*iii*) *The axial rotations of the Earth and Mars*   The rotation of the Earth upon its axis, which produces the regular alternation of light and darkness, also provides us with a natural unit of time—the *day* with its subdivisions—in terms of which we can measure other such processes, for example, the period of rotation of some other planet. Such measurements, repeated from time to time, should show whether that planet in its rotation is speeding up or slowing down with the lapse of time or maintaining a constant period. But all this assumes that the *Earth* is rotating uniformly; for if it is slowing down and the day is growing longer, then any independent process such as a planet's rotation will to that extent appear to be going faster, while, if the day is becoming shorter it will seem as if such a process were slackening its pace.

Writing in 1780 to his friend William Watson, who communicated the letter to the Royal Society, Herschel expressed concern that no astronomer had yet looked into the question of whether the Earth's diurnal motion was strictly 'equable', or uniform (*Phil. Trans.* (1781), 115ff.). The difficulty lay in finding some unquestionably uniform measure of time with which the Earth's rotation could be compared; even the finest available clocks could not provide a standard sufficiently precise to show up inequalities which might, nevertheless, be of practical importance. The best course appeared to be to determine the periods of other planets in terms of that of the Earth, leaving it to future astronomers to ascertain whether these periods maintained the same relative values, and if they did not, to assign a reason.

The fundamental method of determining a planet's period of rotation is (as we have seen) to identify some permanent mark on its surface and to measure the time required for this mark to be carried right round and brought back to the same position again. When it came to selecting planets for this purpose, Herschel's choice was restricted to Mars and Jupiter. Mercury shows no conspicuous surface markings, and the period of Venus is unknown to this day; Saturn, too, is almost featureless, and Herschel's researches on this planet belong to a later period. Jupiter is girdled about his equator with broad belts corresponding, as Herschel suspected, to the tropical region of the Earth where the trade winds prevail. The planet's markings, in fact, appeared to float in an atmosphere undergoing what is called a 'planetary circulation', and therefore could not serve to define the period of Jupiter with the necessary accuracy. Mars, however, was ideal for Herschel's purpose; and his observations indicated a period of 24 hours, 37 minutes, 26·3 seconds (a modern estimate gives 24 hours, 37 minutes, 22·6 seconds).

When Herschel wrote, the question of whether the Earth turned uniformly on its axis was already in the air. Towards the end of the seventeenth century Halley had pointed out that the Moon appeared to be travelling faster in its orbit as the ages passed. Immanuel Kant, the German philosopher, suggested in 1754 that in reality the Earth's rotation was being slowed down by the friction of the tides, acting upon the Earth like a brake, so that the day was becoming longer. Consequently the space described by the Moon in one day would be increased proportionately; and we should form the impression that the Moon was moving faster. After much debate this view has prevailed. We do not know whether Herschel was acquainted with Kant's speculation; but in his letter of 1780 he put forward an argument of his own for the view that 'when the Earth assumed the present form, the diurnal rotation was somewhat quicker than it is at present'. It had been established earlier in the eighteenth century that the roughly spherical Earth is in fact slightly flattened at the poles; and this deformation was plausibly attributed to the forces set up by the Earth's rotation. Herschel noted that the observed degree of flattening corresponded to a more rapid rotation than that now operative; and this suggested to him that the day had become longer in the course of the ages.

(*iv*) *The axis, figure, and polar caps of Mars*   All the heavenly bodies that we get a chance of examining properly are found to be rotating about axes which change but slowly with the lapse of time. It is one of the astronomer's tasks to determine the directions of such axes in space. For the Sun this was effected in the early days of telescopic observation by noting the course of the sunspots across the solar disc at various times of the year. For Mars the surface markings might have served a similar purpose; but because the disc appeared so small, Herschel, when he sought to determine the Martian axis, thought it safer to work from measurements upon the two white spots supposed to mark the planet's poles (*Phil. Trans.* (1784), 233ff.). His observations, extending over the years 1777 to 1783, convinced him that the spots were inconstant and not exactly centred upon the poles; but from their oscillations as the planet rotated he deduced the situation of the axis of rotation. He also showed that the waxing and waning of the white spots followed the alternations of the Martian seasons in a manner suggestive of what occurs in the terrestrial polar regions (cf. Pl. 13):

If . . . we find that the globe we inhabit has its polar regions frozen and covered with mountains of ice and snow, that only partly melt when alternately exposed to the Sun, I may well be permitted to surmise that the same causes may probably have the same effect on the globe of Mars; that the bright polar spots are owing to the vivid reflection of light from frozen regions; and that the reduction of those spots is to be ascribed to their being exposed to the Sun. (Ibid., 260)

Herschel clearly perceived the polar flattening of Mars which gives the planet's disc a slightly elliptical form comparable to what the Earth would exhibit; and his judgment on this point was upheld by his friends Patrick Wilson, Blagden, and Aubert. Occasional local changes in the surface appearance of Mars, attributable to floating clouds and vapours, inclined Herschel to the belief 'that this planet is not without a considerable atmosphere'.

(*v*) *The asteroids* Towards the end of the eighteenth century it was pointed out that the distances of the successive planets from the central Sun increased very nearly according to a certain simple numerical rule. They were roughly proportional to the successive terms of a mathematical series—not an arithmetical or a geometrical progression, but something of the kind. However, the scheme had a serious weakness: there was one term of the series to which no known planet corresponded. This deficiency was reflected in the disproportionately wide gap between the orbits of Mars and Jupiter; and a group of astronomers banded themselves together to search for the planet which, it was felt, *ought* to occupy this vacancy in the solar system. On the first evening of the new century (1 January 1801) an Italian astronomer, Giuseppe Piazzi (not himself a member of the search-party), discovered an object of the eighth magnitude moving slowly among the stars of the constellation Taurus. It proved to be a planet revolving between the orbits of Mars and Jupiter; and it was eventually named Ceres after the tutelary goddess of Sicily, where Piazzi had his observatory. The object was lost for a time in the Sun's rays; but the few observations already made of its movements sufficed for the young mathematician C. F. Gauss to calculate its orbit, so that when it appeared again in the night sky astronomers knew where to look for it, and it was rediscovered at the end of 1801.

It is at this point that Herschel comes into the story.

Early in 1802 he began to search for the new planet in the region of the heavens where he believed it to be; but his efforts were unrewarded until he was informed of its exact position by the Astronomer Royal, Nevil Maskelyne. He first saw it on 7 February 1802; but only after observing the wanderer for a week could he discern the minute disc which distinguishes a planet from a star. The disc appeared faintly ruddy and its apparent diameter roughly one-fifth of that of the Georgian planet (Uranus), which suggested that the object must be very small for a planet (*Scientific Papers*, I, cix ff.).

By the time Herschel next reported on his observations of Ceres, another object of the same kind had been discovered, this time by Heinrich Olbers, a physician and amateur astronomer of Bremen, who gave his find the name of Pallas. Using his lucid-disc micrometer (see p. 91), Herschel tried to determine the angular diameters of these two elusive members of the solar system; thence, knowing their approximate distances from the Earth, he could calculate their diameters in miles (*Phil. Trans.* (1802), 213ff.). But his technique was unequal to the difficulties (formidable even today) of measuring images so small, and possibly non-circular, and which usually appeared a little fuzzy: there were also optical complications which he was only just beginning to understand.

Herschel was uncertain whether to class Ceres and Pallas as planets or as comets. They revolved round the Sun in normal planetary orbits and in the same direction as the other planets; but their sizes were negligible by planetary standards; their orbits were inordinately close to each other and were inclined at considerable angles to the zodiacal plane to which the other planets broadly adhered; and they showed no signs of possessing atmospheres or satellites. On the other hand they had few of the characteristic properties of comets. Perhaps they could be likened to periodically returning comets at their greatest distances from the Sun. In the end Herschel decided to put Ceres and Pallas in a class by themselves. He wanted to name them after some property that particularly distinguished them; and as, even in a good telescope, they looked very much like stars, he called them *asteroids*, 'star-like' bodies.

Writing to Herschel on 17 June 1802, Olbers suggested very tentatively that Ceres and Pallas might be two fragments of a planet formerly occupying an orbit between Mars and Jupiter, but disrupted, perhaps millions of years ago, by an internal explosion or by a collision with a comet. This would explain why (as several Continental astronomers had noticed) the two little planets varied in their relative brightness from night to night, as if reflecting the Sun's light from irregularly shaped rotating masses (*The Herschel Chronicle*, 273).

Herschel thought it probable that further asteroids would be discovered in course of time; he was therefore not surprised when in 1804 the German astronomer K. L. Harding detected another member of this class, which received the name of Juno. Once again Herschel was indebted to Nevil Maskelyne for information which enabled him to pinpoint the star-like object in the heavens and to class it confidently with Ceres and Pallas (*Phil. Trans.* (1805), 31ff.). It showed no real disc: its angular diameter, he concluded, could not therefore amount to as much as half a second. In preparing to determine, with a 10-foot reflector, the angular diameter of 'Mr Harding's asteroid', Herschel carried out a series of experiments to find what was the smallest planetary disc that could be seen as such with the instrument, and what degree of magnification was required to render its circular shape unmistakable to the eye of the observer. More generally

Plate 10 The second speculum of Herschel's
40-foot telescope.

Plate 11 Zone clock for indicating the limit of a
sweep ; used with Herschel's 40-foot telescope.

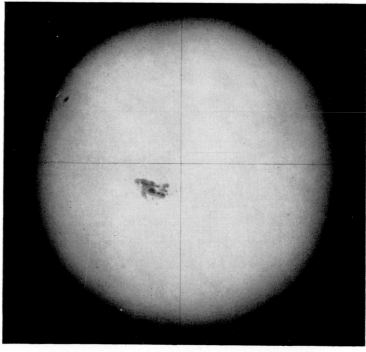

Plate 12 The Sun photographed on 3 February 1905, showing sunspots.

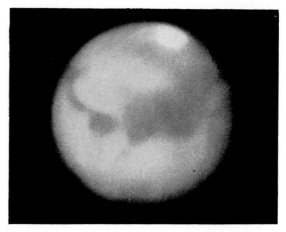

Plate 13 The planet Mars, photographed with the 100-inch telescope, showing the white polar cap.

he wanted to know what factor it is in a telescope that sets a limit to the possible refinement of a measurement of this kind: is it the aperture, the focal length, or the magnification? He tested his telescope upon a series of tiny balls— pin-heads and globules of silver, sealing-wax, pitch, etc.— graduated in order of size. Their dimensions and their distances from the telescope were accurately measured so that the angle they subtended at the observer's unaided eye was known; and the magnification needed to make them appear as discs was noted. The smallest such angle capable of being estimated with the telescope was of the order of one- or two-tenths of a second of arc. Herschel had long been aware that a source of light, whether artificial or a star, which was too small or distant to appear in the telescope as a disc in its own right, nevertheless gave rise to a 'spurious disc', a term still applied to this phenomenon. He noticed that this disc contracted as the magnification was increased, but that it expanded when the effective aperture of the telescope was reduced by covering the outer portion of the mirror with a ring-shaped screen. On the other hand, the effect of covering the central portion of the mirror was to diminish the size of the spurious disc below what it was when the whole mirror was open. In this manner a real planetary disc could be distinguished from the spurious one which might mask it. Spurious discs have been explained on the wave theory of light, according to which a point source produces in the telescope, not a point image, but a minute disc surrounded by concentric rings alternately bright and dark which rapidly fade out with increase of distance from the central maximum.

Yet another asteroid was discovered in 1807, again by Olbers. The news reached Herschel and he commenced his search the same evening; once again it was precise information from Maskelyne that enabled him to track the

F

wanderer down (*Phil. Trans.* (1807), 260ff.). Viewed through a telescope, Vesta (for so the object was named by its discoverer) showed no real disc to distinguish it from a star, nor any nebulosity; and Herschel did not hesitate to include it in the now established class of asteroids.

(*vi*) *Saturn, the ringed planet*   When Galileo directed his recently invented telescope to the planet Saturn, he was aware of something peculiar in the appearance of this member of the solar system. It seemed to possess a pair of appendages, or 'handles', which mysteriously faded from view as the years passed. The phenomenon was explained in 1656 by the Dutch scientist Christiaan Huygens. Using a superior instrument he could distinguish a thin, flat, circular ring surrounding Saturn; he also detected the planet's principal satellite, Titan. A few years later four more satellites were discovered by G. D. Cassini, an Italian astronomer who was to settle in Paris. He also noticed that Saturn's ring consists of two concentric rings of unequal breadth and separated by a dark space which later came to be called the 'Cassini division'.

Herschel devoted seven complete papers to his studies on Saturn, covering the period from 1790 to 1806. In a postscript to his second catalogue of nebulae and star clusters of 1789 he announced his discovery of a sixth satellite of the planet (the existence of which, however, he had suspected two years earlier). Before he could communicate fuller particulars to the Royal Society at their November meeting he had found a seventh satellite (*Phil. Trans.* (1790), 1ff.). In the course of observations dating from 1774 and described in this first paper, he had followed the vicissitudes of the ring, now opening out to present the appearance familiar to us, now contracting to a narrow line across the planet's disc, according to the aspect in which it was presented to his view. He noticed only one black belt in the ring (Cassini's) and he denied the existence of others (such as the one Encke later detected). This belt could not be a shadow; he would not at first assume that it was a division between two concentric rings (as we now suppose it to be), but this might be established by some day observing a star through the division. His observations suggested that the ring must be extremely thin; and he thought it was probably rotating, which would help to relieve the stress of its tremendous weight. It is uncertain whether Herschel ever noticed Saturn's 'crape ring', the dark inner fringe of the annular system. One of his drawings of the planet appears to show this feature (Pl. 16). Herschel never attained to the modern view of Saturn's ring, anticipated by the obscure Thomas Wright forty years earlier: 'Could we view Saturn through a Telescope capable of it, we should find his Rings no other than an infinite Number of lesser Planets, inferior to those we call his Satellites' (*Original Theory*, 65).

Herschel paid much attention to the bright and dark belts to be seen on Saturn's disc, generally lying parallel to the plane of the ring. They reminded him of the belts on Jupiter and suggested the presence of a cloud-bearing atmosphere. This impression was strengthened by the curious behaviour of the satellites which, in passing behind the planet, often 'hung on the limb', remaining for some time optically visible though geometrically concealed, an effect suggesting a refraction of their rays through an atmosphere. Again, the existence of the belts, and changes in their appearance, pointed to a rotation of the planet upon an axis perpendicular to the general plane of the belts and of the ring. Rotation about just such an axis was also suggested by the noticeably elliptic shape of Saturn's disc. Herschel was puzzled by the appearance from time to time of bright spots or protuberances on Saturn's rings. An analysis of these phenomena suggested a rotation of the ring in a period of about ten and a half hours (*Phil. Trans.* (1790), 427ff.); but, as we shall see, the underlying hypothesis of the ring as a solid body has now been abandoned.

The motion of Saturn over half its orbit in about fifteen years enabled Herschel, in the course of time, to examine both the lobes into which the ring is divided by the orbital plane and to establish that the dark belt extends continuously and uniformly right round the ring. By the end of 1791 he had come round to the view that this belt (which appeared of the same hue as the night sky) did indeed represent a division of the ring into two parts of unequal breadth (*Phil. Trans.* (1792), 1ff.). These might well have different periods of rotation in general conformity to Kepler's third Law (which connects the period of a satellite with its distance from its primary). In fact, if the whole ring were to rotate in one piece, severe mechanical stresses would be set up between the outer and the inner portions.

Herschel confirmed what earlier observers had discovered, that the fifth satellite of Saturn varies in brightness, and that the variations occur regularly in the same period as that required for the satellite to revolve round the planet. It was usual in Herschel's day to regard a variable star as a rotating object of irregular shape or having a surface not uniformly bright all over. Herschel suspected that the satellite was such an object rotating on its axis in exactly the same period as that of its orbital revolution. Our Moon's rotation and revolution agree likewise; and Herschel suspected that 'a certain, uniform plan is carried on among the secondaries of our solar system; and we may conjecture, that probably most of the moons of all the planets are governed by the same law; especially if it be founded on such a construction of the figures of the secondaries, as makes them more ponderous towards their primary planets' (ibid., 16). He seems to conceive gravity as acting upon a satellite's distorted shape (the cause of its variable brightness) as if upon a lever, making it always turn the same face to its planet.

With Herschel's study on the fifth satellite of Saturn it may be appropriate to compare his search for variations in the brightness of the four satellites of Jupiter known in his day, upon which he reported about five years later (*Phil. Trans.* (1797), 332ff.). The investigation was complicated by the necessity of comparing the little moons with one another; but he eventually established that they fluctuate in brightness in their respective periods of revolution round Jupiter. It was natural for him to infer that these satellites, too, rotate on axes so as always to turn the same faces to the planet, and that they are not equally reflective in all situations; and these views have been generally sustained.

To return to Saturn: Herschel's observations of five parallel belts on the planet, closely corresponding to those on Jupiter, suggested that Saturn too was rotating, probably rapidly, about its short axis (*Phil. Trans.* (1794), 28ff.). A month later he announced the planet's period as about 10 hours, 16 minutes. (A modern estimate gives 10 hours, 14 minutes, with an uncertainty of about one minute, the period increasing slightly with the Saturnian latitude.) He reached this figure by detecting and analysing the cycle of almost imperceptible variations which the planet's rotation produced in the appearance of certain belts on its surface (*Phil. Trans.* (1794), 48ff.).

In his later observations of Saturn, Herschel noticed that the planet's disc seemed to be of a peculiar shape, abnormally flattened towards the poles and the equator, with the greatest curvature occurring at about the forty-fifth parallel of latitude, an effect, perhaps, of the attraction of the ring

(*Phil. Trans.* (1805), 272ff.). There seemed also some indications of seasonal changes of colour occurring alternately at the two poles; these changes, taken with the zonal markings on the planet, seemed once again to point to the existence of a Saturnian atmosphere.

In the course of his paper on the comet of 1807, Herschel describes a curious bulging appearance affecting the southern polar region of Saturn which he had lately observed; the phenomenon was confirmed by the astronomer's son John Herschel (then fifteen years of age) and by Patrick Wilson. Herschel was satisfied that the phenomenon was an illusion probably caused by the refraction of light-rays travelling to us through an atmosphere which he supposed to envelop Saturn's ring (*Phil. Trans.* (1808), 160ff.). The refractive property of this atmosphere was also invoked to explain why, when the ring, seen edgewise, bisected one of Saturn's small satellites, the little object appeared simultaneously above and below the plane of the ring.

(*vii*) *Uranus and its Satellites* So we come at length to the planet Uranus, the outermost regular member of the solar system known in Herschel's day, which might indeed have claimed our first attention since its discovery inaugurated his career as a professional observer. It was on Tuesday evening, 13 March 1781, while Herschel was examining a region of the heavens in the constellation of the Twins, that he noticed, in the field of his 7-foot reflector, an object which appeared 'visibly larger' than the surrounding stars. Its image, unlike theirs, increased in size as higher magnifications were applied. He recorded it in his Journal as 'a curious either nebulous star or perhaps a comet'; and when next he looked at the object on 17 March he 'found that it is a Comet, for it has changed its place' (in relation to the surrounding stars). He kept it under

observation and reported its movements up to date in a
paper communicated to the Royal Society by his friend
William Watson and read on 26 April (*Phil. Trans.*
(1781), 492ff.). Meanwhile Herschel had, through Watson,
informed the Astronomer Royal, Nevil Maskelyne, of his
discovery. Observing the comet from Greenwich, Maskelyne looked in vain for a tail or other cometary features;
he concluded that it was equally likely to be a planet revolving round the Sun in a nearly circular orbit, and that was
what in due course it proved to be. Herschel wrote to Sir
Joseph Banks requesting that the new-found planet should
be called *Georgium Sidus* (the Georgian Planet) in honour
of his Royal patron and to put future ages in mind that this
star '(with respect to us) first began to shine under His
auspicious reign' (*Phil. Trans.* (1783), 2). But the object
eventually received the name of Uranus.

Herschel employed his lucid-disc micrometer (p. 91)
to estimate the apparent diameter and thence the actual
size of the planet Uranus at its known distance from the
Earth (*Phil. Trans.* (1783), 4ff.). And from time to time
he would direct a telescope to the planet to see if he could
discover any satellites such as were known to attend
Jupiter and Saturn. With an object so remote, and passing
at the time across a background of small stars, success
seemed unlikely; and it was long delayed. However, early
in 1787, having nearly doubled the light reaching his eye
through the adoption of the 'front view' situation of the
eyepiece, he resumed the quest. He soon noticed that two
star-like objects close to the planet were changing their
positions from night to night, in fact they were revolving
round it as satellites in orbits which, as Herschel immediately observed, were inclined at considerable angles
to the ecliptic (*Phil. Trans.* (1787), 125ff.). Intensive
observation of the satellites over more than a year enabled
Herschel to fix their periods, orbital planes, and greatest

distances from Uranus, and thence to deduce (by a standard method applicable to planets possessing one or more satellites) that the mass of Uranus must be about eighteen times that of the Earth (modern estimates give this figure as about 14·7) (*Phil. Trans.* (1788), 364ff.). To simplify the explanation of this method of determining the mass of a planet, assume that the planet and its satellite revolve in circular orbits of known radii and in known periods of revolution. The attraction between the Sun and the planet, and hence the acceleration of the planet towards the Sun, is calculated and put equal to the well-known mechanical expression giving the acceleration of a particle travelling uniformly round a circle, where the radius and period are known. A similar equation is formed for the attraction between the planet and its satellite. The two equations are combined and, after some further approximation, the mass of the planet is obtained in terms of that of the Sun and of other known quantities. The ratio of the Earth's mass to the Sun's is obtained on similar principles, so permitting a direct comparison of the masses of Earth and planet.

In 1797 Herschel reported that he had discovered four additional satellites of Uranus, making six in all (*Phil. Trans.* (1798), 47ff.). This claim was not confirmed, and he was probably deceived by some optical defect of his instrument, though it is possible that he caught confused glimpses of the two faint Uranian moons, Ariel and Umbriel, which describe orbits interior to those of Herschel's authentic pair, Oberon and Titania, and whose existence was definitely established by William Lassell in 1851. (A fifth satellite was detected photographically by G. P. Kuiper in 1948.) In this same paper Herschel announced that the revolutions of the two satellites previously discovered by him were *retrograde*, taking place in the direction opposed to that in which the planets revolve about the Sun and the other satellites then known revolve about their primaries, and in which the Sun and planets rotate upon their axes (so far as information was then available). Herschel also announced at this time that the disc of Uranus appeared to be slightly elliptical, suggesting (by analogy with Jupiter and Saturn) that the planet was in rapid axial rotation. The absence of clearly discernible markings on the planet's disc forbade any direct confirmation of this surmise; and it remained for Dr V. M. Slipher of the Lowell Observatory to establish spectrographically, in 1911-12, that Uranus indeed rotates upon its axis in about ten and three-quarter hours, and that the direction of its rotation agrees with that of the revolution of its satellites. Observations of the two principal satellites of the Georgian planet, extending over some twenty years, enabled Herschel to determine with greater certainty the elements of their orbits. He found these Uranian moons among the most difficult members of the solar system to observe; and the problem of tracking their movements compelled him to study the relation between the space-penetrating and the magnifying powers of a telescope, which jointly determine what he called the *effective* power of the instrument (*Phil. Trans.* (1815), 293ff.).

The equatorial plane of Uranus, which is also the orbital plane of its satellites, is inclined at nearly a right angle to the plane of the ecliptic. If we consider the *supplement* to this angle (exceeding a right angle) as the inclination and suppose that the planet's equator has somehow been tilted through more than ninety degrees, the revolutions of the satellites and the axial rotation of the planet become *direct*, conforming to the rule of the solar system, as exemplified by the eastward rotation of the Earth and revolution of the Moon.

(*viii*) *The comets of 1807 and 1811*   The apparition in 1807 of a bright comet with a conspicuous tail afforded Herschel an opportunity for studying the physical structure of one of these mysterious objects while leaving the determination of its orbit to observers better equipped for that task (*Phil. Trans.* (1808), 145ff.). He distinguished the various parts of the comet: the *nucleus*, a round, uniformly bright disc shading off into the *head*; the nebulous *coma* surrounding the head; and the transparent *tail*. The nucleus appeared solid; and Herschel estimated its diameter at 538 miles. He correctly surmised that the comet did not owe all its illumination to the Sun but shone partly by its own light. Otherwise the nucleus would have appeared in the shape of a nearly full moon, while the coma and the tail, if sufficiently dense to reflect so much light, would have extinguished the light of the stars behind them, which, however, seemed barely dimmed.

Herschel drew up a still more detailed report on the great comet of 1811, one of the most spectacular on record (*Phil. Trans.* (1812), 115ff.). Here, besides the reddish 'planetary body' or nucleus, and the greenish head, there was a surrounding space, dark and transparent, into which the brightness of the head faded and which Herschel conceived as a gaseous atmosphere. Beyond this there was a yellowish *envelope* forming nearly a semicircle, lying on the Sun-ward side of the head and continuing as two streams of light which passed on either side of the head to constitute the magnificent curved tail, roughly estimated to be upwards of a hundred million miles in length. At one stage two concentric envelopes were observed, a characteristic phenomenon in comets of this type. As the comet receded from the Sun Herschel could follow the degeneration of all these spectacular features until the object assumed the form of a 'common globular nebula'.

From these observations Herschel turned to hypotheses as to the structure and origin of the comet of 1811. The nucleus and the head, viewed from various angles during

the weeks of the comet's visibility, always presented circular outlines: they must therefore be globular. Similarly
the bright envelope must be a hollow, hemispherical cap,
visible only where our gaze encounters the greatest thickness of its luminous substance, and therefore appearing as
a semicircular arc. From the rim of this cap proceeds a
conical curtain of the same material which, again, appears
to us as two divergent rays streaming away from the ends
of the envelope to form or to enclose the tail. Herschel
supposed that as the comet, condensed by the cold of outer
space, approached its perihelion (the point on its orbit
where it is nearest to the Sun) the hemisphere exposed
to the solar rays would be heated and some of the comet's
nebulous substance would expand and ascend to a certain
level in its gaseous atmosphere, there, heated to incandescence, to form the bright envelope. 'If we suppose the
attenuation and decomposition of this matter to be carried
on till its particles are sufficiently minute to receive a slow
motion from the impulse of the solar beams, then will they
gradually recede from the hemisphere exposed to the Sun,
and ascend in a very moderately diverging direction towards the regions of the fixed stars' (ibid., 138). This
explanation of the origin of the comet's tail is of great
interest, for it anticipates by nearly a century the modern
explanation of tail-formation by reference to the 'pressure
of light' (radiation pressure), supposed to accelerate
cometary particles away from the Sun. The wastage from
the envelope to the tail, Herschel thought, must be made
good by further emanations from the surface of the comet;
this might well be facilitated by an axial rotation of the
head, exposing all parts of the object in turn to the action
of the Sun's beams.

Herschel supposed that every time a comet passed round
the Sun, or round some other star, it must lose some of the
more volatile materials composing it—it certainly gives

out a lot of light (which was then conceived as a possible product of chemical decomposition) as well as the matter needed to form the tail. Some comets, he thought, might well have made such a perihelion (or 'periastron') passage more often than others and might be expected to show more evident signs of exhaustion. Was that why the comet of 1807 gave a less spectacular display than that of 1811? Are some comets, then, older than others; or do comets, which seem so closely to resemble nebulae, make good their losses by collecting what Herschel called 'unperihelioned' material from any nebulae they encounter in their wanderings through space? Or could a comet *be* a nebula, condensed by passing close to a succession of stars and eventually arriving in the neighbourhood of the Sun?

A striking contrast to the great comet of 1811 was presented by another which appeared in the same year, in time for Herschel to compare the two objects. It showed a bright, round head, distinct from its surrounding *chevelure* (a 'head of hair'), and only the ghost of a tail. It seemed to be of a planetary size and consistency and to shine by reflected sunlight. The presence of the chevelure argued a spherical atmosphere. The faintness of the tail suggested an object which had lost most of its 'unperihelioned' matter and was but little more affected by its approach to the Sun than a planet would have been.

Chapter 4

Herschel's Contributions
to Astronomy—2

1 Variable Stars

Turning now to Herschel's pioneer researches in stellar astronomy, we may conveniently begin with his studies on certain special classes and properties of stars before going on to consider his work on the vast sidereal systems in their present state of organization or in their supposed evolution through the ages. The first paper of Herschel's to be published in the *Philosophical Transactions* dealt with the behaviour of a remarkable star which might stand as the somewhat eccentric representative of a whole class of celestial objects and his observations of which we shall now summarize. As Herschel was not yet a Fellow of the Royal Society, this paper was communicated to it by his friend William Watson (*Phil. Trans.* (1780), 338ff.).

It has been known for centuries that there are stars which do not shine with a steady light. Some of them show periodic changes in brightness which they repeat with clock-like precision; others vary less regularly, and some behave in a completely unpredictable manner. They are known as 'variable stars'; and one of the most remarkable objects of this kind, and among the earliest to be discovered is the so-called Mira Ceti, or 'wonderful star', in the constellation of the Whale. It seems to have been first detected and described by the Friesian astronomer David Fabricius; and it varies so considerably in brightness that sometimes

81

it appears as a star of the second magnitude while at other times it is invisible to the naked eye. Herschel's early observations of this object, extending from October 1777 to February 1780, were generally consistent with those of earlier astronomers in assigning to the variability of Mira Ceti a period of about 312 days (to which, however, the star does not strictly adhere). Herschel continued to keep an eye on Mira Ceti. He again reported upon its vagaries in 1781 (to the Bath Society) and in 1791 (to the Royal Society): his later observations seemed to point to a period of about 331 days for the light-cycle of the exorbitant star.

Already in Herschel's day astronomers were trying to account for this strange phenomenon of variable stars; and he refers to two of the most widely accepted views. Such a star could be conceived as a disc slowly turning about a diameter: it would appear brightest whenever its flat surface was turned towards us, and it would be faintest, or invisible, whenever it was presented to us edgewise. Similar considerations determine the visibility of Saturn's ring. Or perhaps the star was a rotating sphere whose surface was not of the same brightness all over (it might be spotted like the Sun), so that as it turned upon its axis the brighter and the dimmer portions were alternately presented to our view. The occasional appearance or disappearance of spots on the star would produce more irregular changes in its brightness.

Later, as we shall see in the next section, Herschel developed a technique for discovering stellar variables by ranging a selection of nearly equally-bright stars in ascending order of brightness and then watching for disturbances in that order. By an application of this procedure he proved that the brightness of the star Alpha Herculis shows a regular fluctuation having a period of about 60 days. This discovery seemed in some degree to bridge the gap between short-period variables such as Algol (period about 69 hours) and long-period ones such as Mira Ceti (331 days), and thus to bring all the variables into a single class of rotating, spotted globes, of which the Sun could be regarded as a typical member.

2 Stellar Magnitudes

Herschel devoted much attention to the problem of classifying the stars according to their different degrees of apparent brightness. The indications in the star lists of his day were based upon the traditional system of stellar magnitudes established, as we have seen, by Hipparchus and Ptolemy. Herschel started out from the simple working-assumptions that the stars were all of much the same intrinsic brightness as the Sun and that they were distributed through space with a roughly uniform density (*Phil. Trans.* (1796), 166ff.). That would explain why there are a limited number of first-magnitude stars (our nearest stellar neighbours) and why the stars classified under successively higher magnitudes become steadily more numerous: it is because they are distributed over the surfaces of concentric spheres of ever greater radii. Herschel thought there should be four times as many second-magnitude as first-magnitude stars. For, in the absence of any precise definition of stellar magnitudes, and with no idea of the psycho-physical issues involved (such as the relation between the physical intensity of light and the intensity of the sensation it produces in the observer) he felt free to premise that stars of the second, third, fourth etc. magnitudes were in general two, three, four, etc. times as far from the Sun as is a star of the first magnitude. But on applying to the third and higher orders of magnitude his assumptions as to the uniform brightness and spacing of the stars, he found them too far from the facts to be useful. There seemed therefore no objective standard for magnitude classifications; and those embodied in the existing catalogues, notably Flamsteed's, showed serious inconsistencies and could not afford a basis for deciding (at least so far as the fainter stars were concerned) whether a star had in fact changed its brightness since the catalogue was compiled.

Herschel accordingly set himself to arrange groups of stars, selected from some constellation, in short sequences showing a finely graduated increase (or decrease) in brightness from the first to the last star of the sequence. Any future alteration in the brightness of any one of these stars would then reveal itself through a disturbance in the order of the sequence. Herschel commenced working to this plan about 1782; and he acquired great skill in distinguishing fine degrees of luminosity. Writing a century later, the great American astronomer E. C. Pickering remarked: 'Herschel furnished observations of nearly 3000 stars, from which their magnitudes a hundred years ago can now be determined with an accuracy approaching that of the best modern catalogues' (*Harvard Annals*, 23 (1890), 231). The paper under discussion concludes with the first instalment of Herschel's 'Catalogue of the Comparative Brightness of the Stars', classified according to constellations. Five later instalments appeared, the last two posthumous, covering in all about three thousand stars (*Phil. Trans.* (1796), 452ff.; (1797), 293ff.; (1799), 121ff.; Series A, 205 (1906), 399ff.).

To return for a moment to the subject of variable stars: Herschel's investigations on stellar brightness convinced him that many stars had suffered changes of lustre even in the preceding two centuries, perhaps as many as a hundred out of the three thousand examined. And he rightly suspected the existence of many 'periodical stars' whose range of variability was too restricted to strike a casual observer. He regarded such changes as being of much more than merely academic interest. For the Sun is a star; and upon the constancy of its radiance depends the very existence of the animal and vegetable creations. Only by observing the fate of other stars can we estimate the probability of our Sun's waxing or declining or, perhaps, turning into a 'periodical star' with a period of about 25 days. 'Many phenomena in natural history seem to point out some past changes in our climates. Perhaps the easiest way of accounting for them may be to surmise that our Sun has been formerly sometimes more and sometimes less bright than it is at present' (*Phil. Trans.* (1796), 186).

Herschel suggested keeping a check on the intensity of the solar radiation by setting up some kind of photometer (perhaps an ordinary thermometer would serve the purpose) upon some high mountain peak, where it would be unaffected by causes producing casual atmospheric disturbances of the temperature. It fell to the astronomer's son to undertake pioneer investigations on the solar radiation during his expedition to the Cape some forty years later.

Several of the Royal Society astronomers, who found a spokesman in Maskelyne, dissented from Herschel's working-assumption that all the stars were equal in real brightness to one another and to the Sun. He replied that men (or oak trees), taken one with another, define a fairly precise standard of height. Individual members of a species may depart from the standard size, but only within certain limits; and the average height of a score of such individuals would show good agreement with the standard. Such regularity in the sizes of members of a biological species might well be supposed to hold good of the stars.

3 *Stellar Parallax*

When Herschel entered upon his career as an observer of the heavens he almost immediately turned his attention to

G

the classic problem of determining how far distant are the stars from the solar system. This problem, as we have seen, is bound up with the measurement of the parallax which the Earth's orbital motion should produce in the stars; and great practical difficulties still barred the way to its solution. Several of Herschel's predecessors (and notably James Bradley half a century earlier) had sought, without success, to establish the annual fluctuations which such parallax should produce in the meridian altitudes of stars transiting near the zenith of the place of observation. Herschel was anxious to avoid certain sources of error which might seriously affect the accuracy of this method; and he recommended a different procedure in the paper which Sir Joseph Banks communicated for him to the Royal Society in December 1781 (*Phil. Trans.* (1782), 82ff.).

In his quest for stellar parallax Herschel proposed to utilize certain celestial objects known as 'double stars'. The stars are not uniformly distributed over the sky, and they show a marked tendency to form close pairs or groups. What appears to the eye as a single star can often be resolved with the aid of a telescope into two or more barely separable points of light. Their apparent proximity to each other may be a geometrical accident, as when a cow on the horizon appears close to the setting Sun because both happen to lie in roughly the same direction from the observer, though at very different distances. The two members of a close stellar pair often differ greatly in brightness; and on Herschel's natural assumption that, broadly speaking, all stars are equally bright in themselves, this difference in brightness would imply a corresponding difference in the distances of the two components of the pair. Now, as we have seen, stars at different distances from the solar system would be unequally affected by any annual parallax due to the Earth's orbital motion; and therefore a 'double star', as such a stellar pair is called, might afford a sensitive test of the existence of such parallax. It would be sufficient to measure the fine separation of the two images in the telescope at various times of the year and to see whether it exhibited the expected type of annual fluctuation. Galileo, as Herschel acknowledges, had suggested in his great *Dialogue* of 1632 (third Day) that the annual motion of the Earth might be confirmed by establishing such a differential parallax between a bright and a faint star situated near to each other in the heavens.

Suppose, then, that A and B are two stars lying nearly in the same direction as viewed from the Sun S but at widely different distances (Fig. 8). Let the plane which contains A, B, and S cut the Earth's orbit in the two diametrically opposite points O and E. Suppose that when the Earth is at O a terrestrial observer measures the angle AOB which appears to separate the two stars, and that when six months later the Earth is at E he measures the corresponding angle AEB. Then if these two angles are different it is reasonable to assume that the nearer of the two

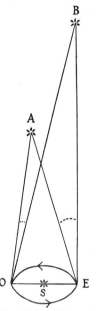

Fig. 8 The differential parallax of a double star

stars has suffered a differential parallax relatively to the more distant. (Of course one or both stars may have moved slightly in the sky during the six months since the observer was at O. To eliminate this source of error he must wait until he is again at O and remeasure the angle AOB: if this angle has changed in the course of the year, a proportionate correction must be applied to the angle AEB.)

In his paper of 1781 Herschel works out detailed rules

for calculating, from the measured differential parallax of two stars of known magnitudes, the absolute parallax, and hence the distance from us (in arbitrary units), of a star of any given magnitude. The apparent brightness of the stars comes into the problem. In the absence of any scientific classification of the stars with respect to their brightness, Herschel proposed the adoption of a peculiar system of stellar magnitudes according to which 'a star of the second, third, or fourth magnitude is two, three, or four times as far off as one of the first'. His assumptions were faulty; and in any case he was no more successful than his predecessors in discovering the stellar parallax. That elusive phenomenon was first detected sixteen years after his death.

4 Double Stars

When Herschel had conceived the idea of establishing parallax in double stars, he undertook a series of 'reviews' of the heavens largely for the purpose of discovering and cataloguing these objects. His earliest review was carried out with a 7-foot Newtonian telescope of 4·5 inches aperture: it extended down to stars of the fourth magnitude. The second review, begun in the summer of 1779 with a 7-foot instrument of 6·2 inches aperture, extended to stars of the eighth magnitude; it provided materials for Herschel's first catalogue of double stars (*Phil. Trans.* (1782), 112ff.), besides affording occasion for his historic discovery of the planet Uranus. The third review of the heavens, begun at the end of 1781, was undertaken with the same instrument; but, whereas he had previously used magnifications of about 220, he now employed powers ranging up to above 6,000. This review took in all the stars of Flamsteed's catalogue, together with others extending at least as far as the twelfth magnitude. It embraced many thousands of stars: Herschel would often examine as many as four hundred in the course of a night's work. He sought to identify any stars included in Flamsteed's catalogue, noting their colours. The principal fruit of this operation was a second catalogue of double stars, presented at the end of 1784 (*Phil. Trans.* (1785), 40ff.). A further instalment, bringing the total of doubles up to 848, proved to be Herschel's last paper (*Mem. Astron. Soc.*, 1 (1822), 166ff.). Besides double stars Herschel's lists contain multiple groups consisting of three or more members.

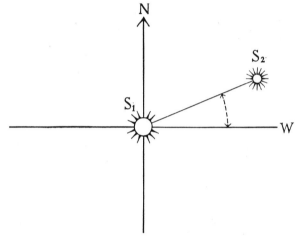

Fig. 9 A catalogue of double stars records the arc S_1S_2 separating the members of a close pair of stars and the position angle S_2S_1W of the fainter member.

In listing these objects Herschel identified each by giving its designation in Flamsteed's catalogue (or by otherwise indicating its position); and he recorded (i) the angle subtended at the eye by the arc joining the pair of stars as measured with a micrometer, and (ii) the 'position angle' which this arc made with an ideal circle parallel to the celestial equator and passing through the brighter star of the pair (Fig. 9). He also noted the comparative brightness of the two stars, and their colours, which often present striking contrasts. Herschel classified his double stars according to their degrees of separation; and he included in his catalogues even pairs of stars separated by one or two minutes of arc, for though these were too widely sundered to be suited to the investigation of annual parallax, yet they might serve another purpose that he already had in mind, that of establishing the motion of the Sun and its train of planets through space. Such a motion might be expected to produce what Herschel called a 'systematical parallax', or what is now called a 'secular parallax', in the stars—a *progressive* alteration, year after year, in the apparent relative positions of stars at different distances from the Sun. And measurements of this secular parallax might enable the speed and direction of the Sun's motion through space to be estimated. To this problem we shall return in the next section.

In measuring up double stars Herschel acquired much experience of micrometers with all their imperfections. Mechanical defects apart, even the finest silk thread was too coarse for setting exactly across the centre of a star image; and measurements made with such threads, especially when in close proximity to each other, were apt to be falsified by illusions arising, as we now know, from the wave structure of light. For the same reason the star images, which should ideally have been mere points of light, appeared as spurious discs with diameters varying according to circumstances. And the necessary illumination of the wires was sometimes too bright for the faint stars which it was desired to measure.

To surmount these difficulties Herschel devised what he called his Lamp Micrometer (*Phil. Trans.* (1782), 163ff.). This was essentially an *artificial* double star, to be set up at a convenient height and distance facing the observer so that, as he observed a real double star with his right eye applied to the eyepiece of his Newtonian reflector, he could view the two artificial point-sources of light of the apparatus with his unaided left eye, and could adjust their separation and alignment until they coincided in his vision with the members of the celestial pair. Dividing the actual separation of the sources by their distance from the observer gave their angular separation; and dividing this by the magnifying-power of the telescope, he obtained the angular separation of the components of the double star.

The apparatus consisted of a 9-foot stand to which was attached, at an adjustable height, a semicircular board having pivoted at its centre a radial arm which could be raised or lowered by turning a long handle (Pl. 17). At the centre of the board there was a lamp; and a second lamp could be moved up and down the arm on a slide by turning another handle. Each lamp shone through a pin-hole to give a star-like point of light.

Besides its application to double stars Herschel also found his lamp micrometer useful in determining the apparent diameters of the planets, or, more questionably, of the stars. At first he would make the separation of the pinholes just equal to the apparent diameter required; but later, applying the instrument to the planet Uranus, he hit upon the idea of substituting for the two sources a single lamp shining through a circular aperture cut out of pasteboard and covered with paper so as to simulate the disc of the planet (*Phil. Trans.* (1783), 4ff.). This was called a lucid-disc micrometer. By selecting from a graduated series of apertures and shielding the light by the right combination of white and blue sheets of paper, the apparent size, luminosity, and colour of the planet were closely matched. In place of the shining disc Herschel would sometimes experiment with a dark disc on a bright background, or with a luminous ring. His results assigned to Uranus a (linear) diameter of about four and a half times that of the

Earth: we now estimate this uncertain factor at barely four.

To return to double stars: in a remarkable paper on stellar astronomy which he read to the Royal Society in 1767, the clergyman-scientist John Michell had argued that these objects are much too numerous to have arisen by chance from a random scattering of stars over the sky (*Phil. Trans.* (1767), 234ff.). The members of such a pair must in many instances constitute a physically connected system, and they must actually be situated near to each other in space and therefore at roughly the same distance from the observer. And in a memoir which Herschel received from Banks some time after reading his paper on the stellar parallax, Christian Mayer, a Jesuit astronomer of Mannheim, had expressed a similar view. Mayer had been cataloguing many double stars (his list was published in the Mannheim *Acta* for 1780), primarily for the purpose of ascertaining the proper motions of bright (near) stars by reference to their faint (distant) neighbours. But he expressed the view that the fainter member of such a pair might be revolving about its brighter companion, or both about a common centre of gravity. Herschel noted this suggestion at the conclusion of his first catalogue of double stars; but he judged it 'much too soon to form any theories of small stars revolving round large ones'.

However, by 1802 Herschel had come to admit (in the introduction to his nebular catalogue) that 'the odds are very much against the casual production of double stars', and that 'their existence must be owing to the influence of some general law of nature; now, as the mutual gravitation of bodies towards each other is quite sufficient to account for the union of two stars, we are authorized to ascribe such combinations to that principle' (*Phil. Trans.* (1802), 484f.). And he discussed a few of the simpler types of orbital motions which might be exhibited by the members of truly double (or *binary*) stars or of multiple systems.

For about a quarter of a century Herschel patiently continued to make regular measurements of the slowly changing separations and position angles of some fifty star-pairs. And in 1803-4 he was able to prove, for the majority of the stars considered, that the accumulated alterations in their elements arose in all probability from orbital revolutions of the member-stars under their mutual attractions (*Phil. Trans.* (1803), 339ff.; (1804), 353ff.). If a shadow of doubt on the question still remained, it was dispelled by the micrometric measurements of Wilhelm Struve of Dorpat. The close pair of stars designated as Eta Coronae, which was among those studied by Herschel and upon which he would often test the power of his telescopes, was one of the first in which Struve established the mutual revolution of the member-stars (in a period of about forty-two years): upon receiving the news in 1832 John Herschel added to the inscription on his father's tomb a clause referring to 'the vast gyrations of double stars'. And in 1867 he published a synopsis of all his father's measures of these objects.

During Herschel's lifetime, then, it became clear that double stars could make no direct contribution to establishing the long-sought stellar parallax; but the way was opened for the discovery of other interesting properties of these systems. They proved to be subject to the same Newtonian law of gravitational attraction as are the members of the solar system; and the evidence of the operation of this law in the remote depths of space helped to strengthen belief in the essential unity of the cosmos.

In his early papers on parallax and double stars Herschel referred to his use of magnifications of 6,000 and over. This claim was received somewhat incredulously by established astronomers; and William Watson urged him, in his own interest, to explain how these powers were estimated. This he did in a letter to Sir Joseph Banks in which he described the straightforward optical methods by which he and his friend Watson had independently determined these powers (*Phil. Trans.* (1782), 173ff.). Nevertheless, some hesitation regarding Herschel's claims persisted up to about forty years ago. Then in May 1924 Dr W. H. Steavenson, while carrying out a systematic examination of such of Herschel's instruments as were still preserved at Slough, came upon a set of eyepieces fitted with short-focus lenses which there was good reason to regard as among those which had been the subject of dispute. Examination by modern optical techniques fully confirmed the order of the powers which Herschel had claimed for his eyepieces: there was in fact one which, with a 7-foot telescope, would have given a magnification of 7,676 (*Monthly Notices of the Royal Astronomical Society*, 84 (1924), 607ff.).

Herschel used to stress that he had only gradually acquired facility in the use of such powers—the 'art of seeing'—through much experience: 'Many a night have I been practising to see, and it would be strange if one did not acquire a certain dexterity by such constant practice' (letter to Watson, 7 January 1782).

5 *The Sun's Motion through Space*

By the time Herschel began his study of astronomy, more than a score of stars had been found to exhibit 'proper motions' whereby their places upon the celestial sphere showed slow but progressive alterations. It was his conviction from the first 'that there is not, in strictness of speaking, one *fixed* star in the heavens', and that even the Sun, considered as a typical star, must in all probability share in this stellar nomadism.

The possibility that the Sun might be travelling freely

through space had already been discussed by astronomers. Tobias Mayer of Göttingen suggested it in 1760. And Lalande, in the memoir of 1776 from which we have extracted his views on sunspots, had argued that whatever force originally started the Sun rotating on its axis must also have set it moving through space with its train of planets. It would be impossible for the terrestrial observer to detect such a motion

> Unless in the course of centuries the Sun approached appreciably closer to the stars in one quarter of the heavens than to those in the opposite quarter. In that event the apparent distances of the stars from one another would have increased on the one side and diminished on the other, which would show us in what direction the motion of translation of the solar system was taking place. (*Mém. de l'Acad. R. des Sci.* (1776), 513)

Or perhaps the Sun and stars with their planetary systems were in equilibrium with their neighbours; in which case the Sun might be revolving about a universal centre of gravity (ibid., 514). A year later we find Alexander Wilson of Glasgow writing of 'that Grand System of the Universe round whose centre this Solar System of ours, and an inconceivable multitude of others like to it, do in reality revolve according to the Law of Gravitation' (*Thoughts on General Gravitation etc.*, London, 1777). Herschel received a copy of Wilson's tract only a few days before he read his paper of 1783 on the solar motion; and he made mention of it in a footnote appended to the published text of the paper. So the idea of the Sun as voyaging through space, and the technique of investigating the direction of its motion, were not completely undreamed of when Herschel laid his views on the matter before the Royal Society in this classic memoir (*Phil. Trans.* (1783), 247ff.).

He starts out from general mechanical principles, arguing that, if even one star were moving, its gravitational attractions upon its neighbours must be constantly changing, thus upsetting any balance of forces which might have kept these other stars at rest. However, he preferred to reason strictly from the results of observation; and in the course of his third review of the heavens, covering the stars of Flamsteed's catalogue and many others besides, he found what appeared to be abundant evidence of changes in the heavens since that historic star list was compiled. Many stars seemed to have disappeared, or to have changed their magnitudes, or to have sprung into existence during the previous half-century. Not all of these apparent changes could be directly attributed to proper motions; and many of them were later traced to errors in observation or in record. But the total effect of all these mutations was to give Herschel a strong impression of the prevalence of motion in the heavens. Even changes in the brightness of a star might, he thought, be due to the slow rotation of a luminary not uniformly bright all over or perhaps non-spherical in shape, or to the periodic eclipse of a bright star by a dark one.

Coming now to the question of the Sun's possible travel through space, the problem presented itself to Herschel of determining the direction and, if possible, the speed of this solar motion. The best hope of solving this problem appeared to lie in analysing the proper motions of a representative sample of stars selected from all over the sky and including the Sun's nearest stellar neighbours. Herschel surmised that, generally speaking, the proper motion that we observe in a star is made up of two parts, one a real motion of the star itself, and the other an apparent or parallactic motion arising from the travel of the observer with the solar system through space. If the selected stars could all have been regarded as at rest, having no motions of their own, then their *apparent* motions to an observer on the Earth would have been mere reflections of the Sun's travel. In such a parallactic motion the Sun and its system (to recur to our former illustration) would play the part of the moving train, while the surrounding stars would correspond to the trees planted alongside of the line. Herschel explained how any displacement of the Sun from S to S' (Fig. 10) in a line AB

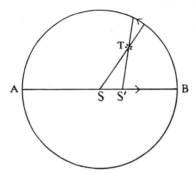

Fig. 10 Parallactic displacement of a star due to the motion of the Sun.

would define two special points on the celestial sphere, namely the point B towards which the Sun is displaced (and which he called the 'apex of the solar motion'), and the diametrically opposite point A (which we call the 'antapex') from which the Sun is receding. Any star T, supposed at rest and not lying in the line AB, must appear, to an observer travelling with the Sun, to have suffered an apparent displacement along a great circle directed away from the apex B and towards the antapex A. This displacement would be directly proportional to the sine of the star's angular distance BST from the apex and inversely proportional to its linear distance ST from the Sun. Conversely, if we observe the stars as tending on the whole to open out from a point in one half of the sky and to close in upon a point in the other half, it is reasonable to regard this as due to a progressive displacement of the solar system; and if we can locate the points with respect to which the stars are diverging or converging, we can define the direction of the solar motion.

However, to complicate matters, each star must be supposed to possess a motion of its own (it is not a tree but a cow running across the field); this motion is compounded with the parallactic shift just mentioned, and there is no obvious way of separating these two components of the proper motion which we observe in any single star. But if a sufficient number of stars be taken into account, their individual motions may be expected to average out, leaving a general shift common to them all and arising from the observer's travel through space. It was on this principle that Herschel set himself to discover the direction of the Sun's proper motion. His original plan was to look for the parallactic shifts which that motion ought to produce between the components of double stars, assuming (as he still did) that the members of such a pair differed in their distance from the observer to the degree suggested by their great difference in brightness. With this purpose in view he listed some three hundred and fifty double stars distributed along three mutually perpendicular zones of the heavens, with a further hundred and twenty lying along the ecliptic. An analysis of changes in the configurations of the stellar pairs, even after so short a period as ten years, might, he hoped afford significant information. In the meantime Herschel undertook to analyse the proper motions of the few stars for which this phenomenon had already been accurately measured. Nevil Maskelyne, the Astronomer Royal, and the French observer Lalande had tabulated proper motions relating to thirteen stars; and Herschel found that these motions could best be accounted for by assuming the solar system to be travelling towards a point upon the celestial sphere somewhere in the neighbourhood of the star Lambda Herculis. The proper motions of forty-four more stars, determined by Tobias Mayer of Göttingen and discussed in a post-script to Herschel's paper, generally pointed to the same conclusion. Stars whose motions contradicted the hypothesis were suspected of belonging to a different system moving as a whole relatively to that of which the Sun is a member. This idea of a 'local cluster' to which the Sun belongs had been suggested by John Michell; it is of particular interest in relation to more recent speculations along these lines.

The speed of the Sun's travel was another question, not so easily answered without information as to the distances of the stars under consideration. By a rather tentative calculation Herschel was led to estimate this speed as not less than that of the Earth in its annual orbit.

In 1805 Herschel returned to the problem of the Sun's travel through space (*Phil. Trans.* (1805), 233ff.). By that time many of the double stars catalogued in earlier years were showing noticeable changes in the relative positions of their components. Herschel still regarded such changes as in the nature of proper motions and as serving to indicate the course of the Sun's voyage through space; and he thought that they supported his conclusions of 1783. Meanwhile Nevil Maskelyne had published the proper motions of thirty-six of the brightest stars. By supposing the Sun to be travelling in such a way as to make the real motions of the six brightest of these stars add up to as small a total as possible, Herschel was led to assign to the apex a position differing from the one he had given to it in his earlier paper but still lying within the constellation Hercules.

We saw how Lalande argued that the force which originally set the Sun rotating must necessarily have imparted to it a motion of translation through space. Herschel accordingly urged astronomers to keep a special watch on stars of variable brightness, particularly on short-period variables such as Algol. For as we have seen, such stars were at that period conceived to be rotating objects of irregular shape or non-uniform surface brightness; and their swift rotation should be accompanied by a correspondingly rapid translation through space, which ought to endow them with appreciable proper motions.

In a sequel to this paper, read nine months later, Herschel tackled the more formidable problem of estimating the speed of the Sun's travel through space (*Phil. Trans.* (1806), 205ff.). He worked on the assumption (to which he was so often forced to resort) that the stars are all of roughly the same brightness *in themselves*, so that the brighter they look the nearer they are. He also assumed that, broadly speaking, the Sun's proper motion, viewed from a star, would be comparable to that of the star, viewed from the Sun. Having no idea of the distances of the stars, Herschel had to work out the Sun's speed, not in miles a second but in arbitrary units. The problem was really beyond him, and it had to await the application of the spectroscope, which enables an observer to measure directly his relative speed of approach to or recession from a luminous source such as a star. However, in the course of his intricate calculations, Herschel found that the individual motions of the thirty-six stars in Maskelyne's list did not seem to be distributed at random in space: the stars showed a marked tendency to move in the same direction as the Sun. He writes:

The similarity of the directions of the sidereal motions is a strong indication that the stars, having such motions, as well as the Sun, are acted upon by some connecting cause, which can only be attraction; and as it has been proved that attraction will not explain the observed phenomena without the existence of projectile motions, it must be allowed to be a necessary inference, that the motions of the stars we have examined are governed by the same two ruling principles which regulate the orbitual motion of the bodies of the solar system. (ibid., 236)

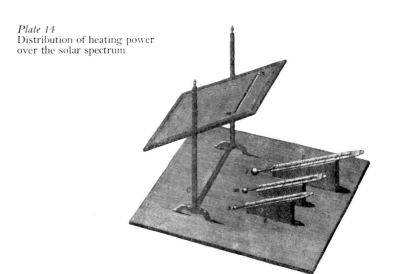

Plate 14
Distribution of heating power
over the solar spectrum.

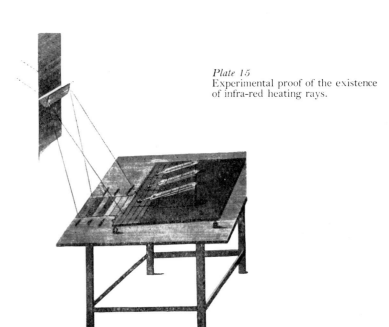

Plate 15
Experimental proof of the existence
of infra-red heating rays.

Plate 16 Herschel's drawings of Saturn (top)
and Jupiter (showing Jupiter's third satellite and
its shadow).

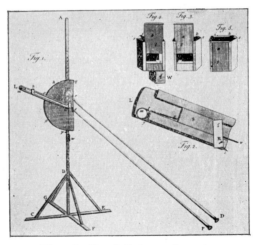

Plate 17 Herschel's lamp micrometer.

Herschel in fact seems to have stumbled on evidence of the preferences which the stars do indeed exhibit for moving in certain directions and which are now explained on the hypothesis that they are revolving round the massive clouds of stars and nebular material forming the centre of the galactic system.

Herschel, as we have noted, was much impressed by the discrepancies between the face of the sky in his own day and the indications of Flamsteed's great catalogue of 1725. The apparent extinction of some stars and the gain or loss of brightness by others suggested the prevalence of change and motion in the heavens. Gradually, however, it dawned upon him how inaccurately the catalogue, published five years after Flamsteed's death, had been compiled; and he recognized the necessity for returning to the original observations from which the star places had been computed and which had been printed in the second volume of the *Historia Coelestis*. At her brother's request Caroline Herschel undertook the arduous task of reducing and indexing all Flamsteed's stellar observations: the work extended over twenty months (*Phil. Trans.* (1797), 293ff.). It was then discovered that one hundred and eleven stars inserted in the catalogue had never been observed by Flamsteed at all, while upwards of five hundred stars which he had completely located, or had sufficiently identified, had been omitted: these were now catalogued and published with Caroline's Index in 1798.

Reference has been made above to Flamsteed's star catalogue; and in the course of the present chapter we have had occasion to mention Herschel's catalogue of double stars and his classification of selected stars in respect of their brightness. On a later page we shall describe his technique for cataloguing the nebulae and star clusters. It may be useful at this point to indicate briefly how the place of a celestial object is defined and recorded in such a

H

way that an astronomer can readily locate it in the heavens
and direct his instrument to it.

All through the ages star catalogues have been constructed on much the same lines as the earliest such list on
record, that drawn up by Hipparchus of Rhodes in the
second century before Christ. To each star is assigned one
line of the catalogue, and the entry extends across three
columns; the first contains a description or symbol serving
to identify the star, and the other columns contain the two
angles, or co-ordinates, required to fix its position on the
sphere of the sky. To understand how this is effected, let
us imagine an observer stationed at the centre of the
Earth and endowed with powers of vision enabling him
to see places on its surface. If he wished to record the
position of any place so as to be able to locate it again, or
to enable some other such *geocentric* observer to do so, it
would be quite sufficient for him to specify its geographi-
cal longitude and latitude. This involves the selection of
the terrestrial equator as the primary circle of reference,
and the point where the equator cuts the meridian through
Greenwich as the zero from which longitude is reckoned.
Every great circle such as the equator possesses a pair of
diametrically opposite poles; and it is along some secondary circle running from the equator towards the poles
that we measure the secondary co-ordinate or latitude
which, with the corresponding longitude, suffices to determine uniquely the exact location of any selected place on
the Earth. We have seen how, for many practical purposes,
stars and other heavenly bodies can be regarded as
situated upon a vast celestial sphere; and their positions
thereon can be defined on the same principle as those of
places on the Earth. In fact the 'geocentric observer'
(located at the centre of the Earth) is a favourite fiction
of astronomers; and the primary circle to which they refer
the places of stars, the celestial equator, is simply the

trace upon the celestial sphere of the terrestrial equator as viewed by such an observer. Corresponding to longitude on the Earth, the primary co-ordinate of a star is its *right ascension,* measured eastward from one of the two so-called equinoctial points. The secondary co-ordinate, or *declination* corresponds to latitude on the Earth and is measured towards one or other of the celestial poles (Fig.

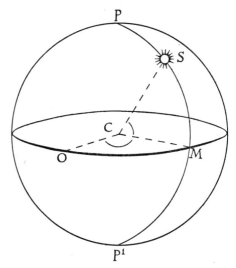

Fig. 11 The position of the star S upon the sphere is defined by reference to the primary great circle OM and a secondary circle SSP¹ passing through the poles of the primary. The star's co-ordinates are the arcs OM, MS or the angles OCM, MCS subtended by these arcs at the eye of the centrally-situated observer.

11). In consequence of the Earth's daily rotation eastward, the celestial sphere appears to turn westward; and the equinoctial point is regarded as the hand of a 24-hour clock measuring out the so-called sidereal time as it performs its daily circuit. Time in fact is involved in the determination of a star's place: the right ascension of a star is expressed in units of time and is numerically equal to the local sidereal time of the star's transit across the observer's meridian.

The observed transit of a known star thus serves for the correction of the observatory clock; the clock for its part indicates at each instant how far any known star is from the meridian, and it gives the right ascension of any unknown star transiting at that moment. The astronomer's equipment must thus include a trustworthy clock; the one used by Herschel in connection with his 40-foot reflector was the gift of his friend Alexander Aubert (Pl. 11). He did not, however, attempt to determine star places with the utmost attainable accuracy, leaving that task to astronomers such as Maskelyne who had at their disposal instruments specially designed for the purpose. And he made considerable use of micrometers to refer the positions of planets or of faint objects to adjacent stars, the positions of which were given in the standard catalogues.

Chapter 5

Herschel's Contributions
to Astronomy—3

1 *The Construction of the Heavens:*
1784 and 1785

Foremost among the problems which engaged Herschel's
attention throughout his career as an astronomer was that
of discovering what he called 'the Construction of the
Heavens', the architecture of the system of stars of which
the Sun is a member. Although he nowhere mentions the
name of Thomas Wright and seems not to have been
acquainted with his book, yet his procedure implied a
similar conception of the nature of the Galaxy. The
principle that the crowding of the stars into any part of the
sky indicated the extent of the stellar system in that
direction was clearly stated in the first of Herschel's
classic papers on this problem, read to the Royal Society
on 17 June 1784 (*Phil. Trans.* (1784), 437ff.). He wrote:

It is very probable that the great stratum, called the Milky
Way, is that in which the Sun is placed, though perhaps not in
the very centre of its thickness. We gather this from the
appearance of the Galaxy, which seems to encompass the whole
heavens, as it certainly must do if the Sun is within the same.
For, suppose a number of stars arranged between two parallel
planes, independently extended every way, but at a given considerable distance from each other; and, calling this a sidereal
stratum, an eye placed somewhere within it will see all the stars
in the direction of the planes of the stratum projected into a great

circle, which will appear lucid on account of the accumulation of the stars; while the rest of the heavens, at the sides, will only seem to be scattered over with constellations, more or less crowded, according to the distance of the planes or number of stars contained in the thickness or sides of the stratum. (ibid., 443)

Herschel gives a diagram (Pl. 18) showing how an observer situated in the heart of a box-shaped stratum, or layer, of stars will see them chiefly projected upon the sky as an encircling ring. He conceives the starry stratum as cleft at one end, not far from the Sun's position, so accounting for the observed division of the Milky Way into two branches which run parallel through the sky for some distance before joining up again. He even tried to connect the Sun's motion through space (which he had so recently been studying) with the supposed configuration of the system of stars. The apex he had indicated for this motion lay not far from where the Milky Way divides into two branches, so constituting a concourse of stars which might well attract in that direction any star situated at no great distance. This hypothesis of a cloven layer of stars would, Herschel supposed, 'satisfactorily, and with great simplicity, account for all the phenomena of the Milky Way, which, according to this hypothesis, is no other than the appearance of the projection of the stars contained in this stratum and its secondary branch' (ibid., 445). This surmise was now to be established upon a statistical foundation.

Herschel worked with a Newtonian reflector of 20 feet focal length and nearly 19 inches aperture. The instrument was restricted to observations in the meridian; but it served for the rough measurement of the position of any selected celestial object. Upon directing this telescope to a bright portion of the Galaxy near the constellation Orion, Herschel found that the luminous cloud was completely resolved into separate small stars of which, on an average, about eighty were simultaneously visible in the field of view. This kind of estimation of star-density in various parts of the sky Herschel called 'gaging the heavens', or the 'star-gage'. It was the principal method that he adopted for determining the shape of the great stratum of stars visible as the Milky Way and locating the Sun's position therein. He would turn his telescope towards one part of the sky after another and count the number of stars visible in the field of view at each setting of the instrument. (In practice he would make ten settings upon fields very near together and take the mean of the ten star-counts.) Assuming that the stars are distributed fairly uniformly throughout the space they occupy, and that the telescope could everywhere penetrate to the boundary of the stellar system (otherwise the contour defined would mark the limit, not of the Universe but of the range of the telescope), then the apparent crowding of the stars in any direction would indicate how far the system of the stars extended in that direction. The purpose of Herschel's star-gauging operations was thus to determine 'the length of a ray revolving in several directions about an assumed point [the Sun] and cut off by the bounds of the stratum'.

From the beginning Herschel connected his speculations on the structure of the stellar system with the riddle of the nebulae, about which he has something to say in this paper of 1784. His attention seems first to have been directed to nebulae and star clusters by his friend Alexander Aubert, who gave him a copy of a catalogue of 103 of these objects compiled by the French astronomer and noted comet hunter Charles Messier, and published in 1783-4. Messier distinguished between nebulae, strictly so called, and star clusters into which thousands of faint stars are crowded like a swarm of bees; but Herschel found that his telescope was sufficiently powerful to reveal many of

Messier's nebulae as star clusters. And he seems to have
felt little doubt, at this stage of his career, that *all* nebulae
would in time be resolved in this manner; we shall see how
he was subsequently compelled to abandon this view.
Herschel's telescope revealed many previously unobserved
nebulae and clusters: these new discoveries already num-
bered 466 when he read his paper. He noticed that the
nebulae, while exhibiting the greatest variety of forms,
showed a tendency to arrange themselves in long bands or
filaments winding their way through the sky; he likened
them to the strata of the Earth's crust. He also observed
that nebulae tended to occur in groups in some parts of the
sky rather than in others; that they were often associated
with fairly bright stars, and that they were interspersed
with starless patches of sky. He learned to recognize the
signs indicating the neighbourhood of nebulae, and would
warn Caroline, on duty at the clock, that he was 'on
nebulous ground'.

In a second paper on the construction of the heavens
Herschel began by asking his readers to imagine what
would happen to a collection of stars of various sizes,
distributed almost uniformly throughout an indefinite
region of space and drawn together by their mutual
gravitational attractions (*Phil. Trans.* (1785), 213ff.).
An unusually massive star would gather its neighbours
round it to form a globular cluster of a familiar type; and
a similar but more irregular grouping would arise from
the attractions of a few ordinary stars which happened to
be bunched together. Combinations of such units would
produce more compound or extensive stellar groupings
such as Herschel believed our galactic system to be. If individual nebulae were supposed to originate in this way it
would be easy to understand why they occurred in associ-
ation with empty spaces from which the original stellar
inhabitants had apparently been swept up. To simplify the

problem Herschel at first represented the stars as being
at rest; but in order to explain why they had not long
since fallen into one another he was willing to endow them
with motion under 'projectile forces', the very agency that
Alexander Wilson had invoked in 1777 to save the stellar
system from collapse. However, the main purpose of this
paper of 1785 was to tabulate the numerical results of
Herschel's star-gauging operations—the numbers of stars
in regions of the heavens visible from his place of observation—and to show that they supported the hypothesis
that we have just outlined. In selecting fields for gauging
he avoided obvious star clusters where his assumption of a
uniform scattering of the stars clearly broke down.

   The length of the ray, or sounding-line into space, indicated by the results of the star-gauges could not be taken
as simply proportional to the number of stars visible in the
field of the telescope when turned in the selected direction.
For those stars represent the contents of a narrow cone
having its vertex at the observer's eye and broadening out
towards its remote base so as to include a greater abun-
dance of stars than was proportional merely to the height
of the cone. Herschel accordingly investigated and solved
the problem of calculating the (relative) depth of the
stellar system from the corresponding star-counts. He hit
upon a convenient way of representing his results graphi-
cally. We are to think of a point S, representing the Sun,
from which is set off, in any direction for which information is available, a straight line SP, measuring upon a
certain scale the distance to which the system of stars extends in that direction. If this is done for one star field
after another, all the end-points such as P should be found
to lie on a closed surface exhibiting in miniature the contour of the galactic system and defining the position of the
Sun therein. It is simpler, however, to think of a section
through such a surface (a section containing the Sun),

such as Herschel furnished in Fig. 12; this distinctly shows the cleavage in the starry stratum to which reference has already been made. In estimating the extent of the sidereal system Herschel assumed as his unit of length the distance of Sirius—the brightest and therefore, in his view, probably the nearest of the stars—and he found the other stars to extend at most to 497 of these units from the Sun: the

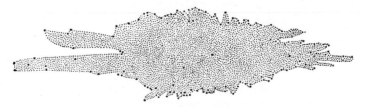

Fig. 12 Section through our sidereal system.

figure depended upon assumptions as to the connection between the distance and the apparent magnitude of a star which had not at that period been cleared up. Herschel's conclusion was that our system of stars was probably a huge *detached nebula*, a vast collection comprising separate stars as well as globular clusters and irregular clusters, everywhere bounded by empty space.

On the supposition that the density of a star cluster was a measure of the period of time during which the component stars had been drawing together, Herschel found reason to suppose that our stellar stratum was a relatively youthful one: this idea of a celestial system as the product of a continuing process was novel and highly significant. He believed that other systems such as ours could be discerned in the heavens, separated from us and from one another by vast tracts of space: 'It may not be amiss to point out some other very remarkable Nebulae which cannot well be less, but are probably much larger than our own system; and, being also extended, the inhabitants of the planets that attend the stars which compose them

must likewise perceive the same phenomena' (ibid., 258).
Thomas Wright too, as we have seen, had surmised that
the 'cloudy spots' barely visible in various parts of the
heavens might be 'external creations', bordering upon the
one we inhabit. Herschel made the interesting observation
that these external nebulae appeared concentrated towards
what we still call the 'poles' of the Galaxy. And again in
this classic paper of 1785 he drew attention to a peculiar
class of celestial objects which he called 'planetary
nebulae' (a name they still retain) because, viewed through
a telescope, they resemble the discs of planets (Pl. 19).

As the years passed, however, the conviction grew upon
Herschel that the stars of our system are not in fact uniformly distributed throughout the space they occupy: 'On
a very slight examination,' he wrote in 1802, 'it will
appear that this immense starry aggregation is by no
means uniform. The stars of which it is composed are very
unequally scattered, and show evident marks of clustering
together into many separate allotments' (*Phil. Trans.*
(1802), 495).

2 Sweeps and Nebular Catalogues

In 1786 Herschel published a catalogue of one thousand
nebulae and star clusters discovered by him since 1783;
and by way of introduction he described the development
of his technique for detecting such objects and establishing
their positions on the celestial sphere (*Phil. Trans.* (1786),
457ff.). He worked with his 20-foot Newtonian reflector
which, when mounted upon its stand, could be elevated or
lowered in the meridian so as to point in any direction
between the horizon and the zenith: it also had a limited
freedom to move in a sideways direction. Standing on a
gallery near the eyepiece, Herschel would draw the telescope from side to side over its limited arc, altering the

elevation of the instrument slightly from time to time, and noting the positions of any objects of interest. But the procedure was confusing and fatiguing; and constant note-taking by lamp-light rendered the eye insensitive to faint objects. Herschel accordingly adopted by degrees a differ-ent method of 'sweeping' (as he called the operation) in which the telescope swept a *vertical* section of the meridian, being elevated or lowered as required by a workman. At the same time the devoted Caroline undertook the task of writing down his observations to his dictation and reading them back to him again, while noting, on conveniently situated dials, the sidereal time and the elevation of the instrument: these quantities sufficed to define the position of the object being observed. The sweeps for nebulae and clusters continued until September 1802; and to this first catalogue of them there were added two others (*Phil. Trans.* (1789), 212ff.; (1802), 477ff.). The classification of these objects was intended to serve practical ends, the nebulae being listed in order of brightness and the clusters in order of density, and a brief description of each being supplied. In his observations of nebulae Herschel made surprisingly little use of his 40-foot telescope, and he missed discovering the spiral forms which many of these objects exhibit and which the great instrument might well have revealed.

3 *Nebulous Stars*

In his paper of 1785 on the construction of the heavens, Herschel gave the earliest description of a class of celestial objects which he called 'planetary nebulae' from the re-semblance which they bore to planets when viewed through the telescope. They appeared as bright, sharply defined discs, circular or slightly oval; some also showed a brighter nucleus. And Herschel, with some hesitation, classed them as nebulae consisting of 'stars that are compressed and accumulated in the highest degree' (*Phil. Trans.* (1785), 265). He had in fact been led by his experience to regard all nebulous appearances in the heavens as 'of a starry nature' and distinguishable as collections of stars when viewed through a sufficiently powerful telescope. He found that he could trace a continuous sequence of appearances ranging from obvious star groups, such as the familiar Pleiades, on through clusters which his telescopes could separate into stars with increasing difficulty, and so finally to milky patches which no instrument at his command could resolve but which he did not doubt were objects of the same nature situated at immense distances from us. He was gradually shaken in this conviction however by noticing, here and there in the heavens, stars surrounded by luminous atmospheres (*Phil. Trans.* (1791), 71ff.). He variously described such a stellar appendage as a 'milky nebulosity' or a 'chevelure' (head of hair); and he could not doubt that it belonged to the star, situated exactly at the centre of its circular aureole. Under date 13 November 1790, for example, he records:

A most singular phenomenon! A star of about the 8th magnitude, with a faint luminous atmosphere, of a circular form, and of about 3 [minutes of arc] in diameter. The star is perfectly in the center, and the atmosphere is so diluted, faint, and equal throughout, that there can be no surmise of its consisting of stars; nor can there be a doubt of the evident connection between the atmosphere and the star. (ibid., 82)

Herschel felt this observation to be a serious challenge to his view on the starry nature of nebulae:

If the nebulosity consist of stars that are very remote, . . . then, what must be the enormous size of the central point? . . . If the star be no bigger than common, how very small and compressed must be those other luminous points that are the occasion of the nebulosity which surrounds the central one? As, by the former supposition, the luminous central point must far exceed the standard of what we call a star, so, in the latter, the shining matter about the center will be much too small to come under the same denomination; we therefore either have a central body which is not a star, or have a star which is involved in a shining fluid, of a nature totally unknown to us. (ibid., 83)

Herschel preferred the latter alternative; and his considered judgment on such objects was 'that the nebulosity about the star is not *of a starry nature*'. He also surmised that the extensive nebulae not intimately connected with stars, such as the great one in Orion, might consist of such a 'shining matter', which he held to be self-luminous and 'more fit to produce a star by its condensation than to depend on the star for its existence'. In fact a planetary nebula might represent the final stage in the formation of a star by the condensation of just such a shining fluid. And perhaps this mysterious substance might itself consist of particles which were, in Herschel's day, believed to constitute light—light emitted by the stars through the ages and now at length being collected and condensed to form new luminaries. However that might be, Herschel henceforward abandoned his earlier assumption that *all* nebulae were distant star clusters ideally capable of being resolved into stars by means of a sufficiently powerful telescope:

We may . . . have surmised nebulae to be no other than clusters of stars disguised by their very great distance, but a longer experience and better acquaintance with the nature of nebulae, will not allow a general admission of such a principle. (*Phil. Trans.* (1811), 270)

4 *The Construction of the Heavens: 1817 and 1818*

In his last papers on the construction of the heavens, presented in 1817 and 1818, Herschel followed a suggestion of the astronomer John Michell and anticipated in some degree the modern technique of investigating the distribution, in depth, of the stars in our celestial locality by merely counting how many of them fall into each successive class of magnitude. To simplify matters he assumed once more that the stars were all of roughly the same brightness in themselves, their differences in magnitude being attributable to differences in their distances from us; that their distribution corresponded to 'a certain properly modified equality of scattering', and that the step from any one magnitude to the next higher (fainter) one corresponded to a certain uniform increase in distance (*Phil. Trans.* (1817), 302ff.). He calculated the proportions in which we should expect to find the stars shared out among the various magnitudes; and he compared these proportions with those actually observed. The brighter stars fell below while the fainter stars greatly exceeded their calculated quotas: this on the face of it suggested that the stars became more densely crowded with increasing distance from the Sun. But of course the magnitudes given in the catalogues bore no strict relation to the actual distances of the stars; and all that could be inferred was that 'taking the stars of each class one with another, those of the succeeding magnitudes are farther from us than the stars of the preceding order.' However, this general conclusion served Herschel as the starting-point for a further investigation which resulted in a more precise definition of stellar magnitudes as orders of distance. Again he assumed the stars to be all equally bright in themselves ('still allowing that all such deviations may exist, as generally take place among the individuals belonging to the same species'); but he now invoked the established physical principle 'that the light of a star is inversely as the square of its distance', so that if 'we can find a method by which the degree of light of any given star may be ascertained, its distance will become a subject of calculation'. Thus if we select a standard star of the first magnitude and adopt its distance from us as our unit, then an intrinsically similar star only one-quarter as bright as the standard star must be two units distant; at three units' distance it would have one-ninth of the brightness, and so on.

Herschel accordingly prepared two 7-foot reflecting telescopes as nearly alike as possible and placed them side by side so that he could look through them in rapid succession. He then cut down the effective aperture of one of them by partly covering the mirror with one of a graduated series of ring-shaped screens and directed it to a standard star. Then with the second instrument (its aperture unrestricted) he examined a variety of stars until he found one whose light appeared equal to that of the standard star viewed through the first instrument. On Herschel's assumptions, the distances of the two stars must be in the proportion of the two apertures under which they appeared of equal brightness. Thus the first magnitude star Arcturus, viewed with half the aperture of the one telescope (and therefore with one-quarter of the mirror exposed), appeared equal to the star Alpha Andromedae viewed with the whole aperture of the other. The latter star, being therefore one-quarter as bright as Arcturus, should be at twice the distance and of the second magnitude (or 'order of distances') in Herschel's system for classifying stellar brightness. Similarly Alpha Andromedae, viewed in turn with half the aperture, appeared equal to Mu Pegasi, which must therefore be of the fourth order of distance. Herschel extended this procedure in an attempt to gauge the limiting order of distance of the stars of the Milky Way. And in the companion paper read just a year later, he applied a corresponding procedure to the problem of the distribution in space of the star clusters (*Phil. Trans.* (1818), 429ff.).

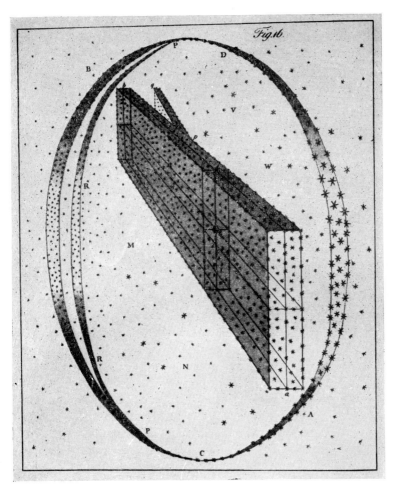

Plate 18 The starry stratum and the Milky Way.

Plate 19 Planetary nebula in Ursa Major (the 'Owl').

However, 'by these observations it appears that the utmost stretch of the space-penetrating power of the 20 feet telescope could not fathom the Profundity of the Milky Way'; and that the great 40-foot instrument would 'probably leave us again in the same uncertainty as the 20 feet telescope'. It thus appeared 'that not only our Sun, but all the stars we can see with the eye, are deeply immersed in the Milky Way, and form a component part of it'. It seems, then, that Herschel could not finally determine whether the Galaxy was a nebula of definite dimensions or whether it was a stratum of stars extending indefinitely in length and breadth as Wright had supposed. It was his lifelong conviction, however, that the galactic system is one of a class of island universes. And in our own day this view has been confirmed.

5 The Evolution of Celestial Systems

One of the principal aims of science is to explain the things and happenings around us so that they do not come at us 'out of the blue' but hang together and fit into a background of familiar experience. And one way of explaining a mysterious object is to exhibit it as a stage, or a product, of a process of development carried through under the operation of familiar natural laws. The best-known example of this mode of explanation is afforded by the theory of organic evolution of which Charles Darwin gave the classic formulation a century ago. Since then this technique has been extended to establish the existence of intelligible order in realms far removed from its original biological field of application. Languages, philosophical ideas, social institutions, even the chemical elements are now generally regarded as evolutionary products. Astronomers, too, often proceed on similar lines in their efforts to re-create in the scientific imagination the process by which sidereal

I

objects have developed through vast periods of time. Already in the eighteenth century naturalistic hypotheses as to the origin and growth of celestial systems had begun to stir in the minds of such thinkers as Buffon, Kant, and Laplace; and in many of Herschel's papers we find cosmic bodies or aggregations conceived as developing under natural forces along prescribed lines.

Among the most beautiful and unmistakable of telescopic objects are the globular star clusters; and in the introduction to his nebular catalogue of 1789 Herschel advanced the view that such a stellar conglomeration, with its characteristic condensation towards the centre, must be the product of some central force (such as gravitational attraction) producing effects proportional to the time of its operation (Pl. 20). He had likened the heavens to 'a luxuriant garden, which contains the greatest variety of productions, in different flourishing beds'; and 'to continue the simile I have borrowed from the vegetable kingdom, is it not almost the same thing, whether we live successively to witness the germination, blooming, foliage, fecundity, fading, withering, and corruption of a plant, or whether a vast number of specimens, selected from every stage through which the plant passes in the course of its existence, be brought at once to our view?' (*Phil. Trans.* (1789), 226).

In one of his later papers on the construction of the heavens, Herschel applied the evolutionary method to the nebulae in an attempt to prove, by an elaborate induction from his accumulated observations, that nebulae develop into stars (*Phil. Trans.* (1811), 269ff.). He classified the hundreds of these objects contained in his own and in Messier's catalogues according to their appearance, breaking them up into so many different classes that the members of one class shaded off imperceptibly into those of the next. The paper is illustrated with figures serving to typify the essential characteristics of each class of nebulae. Beginning with instances of faint, milky nebulosity covering considerable areas of the sky, the classification passes on to smaller patches of this material; thereafter (to abbreviate the list of nebular classes somewhat) the successive types grow more regular in shape, brighter towards the centre, more uniform in surface brightness (the planetary nebulae have their place here), more condensed, until eventually they shrink into objects almost indistinguishable from stars and, as Herschel believed, finish their courses *as* stars. The slightly elliptical figures of many of the planetary nebulae suggested that they must be rotating about axes; and this, too, seemed to link them with stars, which Herschel supposed to be generally in rotation after the manner of the Sun. The agency behind this evolution of nebulae Herschel surmised to be gravitational attraction between their parts.

This paper on the economy of nebulae was supplemented three years later by a similar analysis of the 'sidereal part of the heavens' in which the stars took up the story from where the nebulae had left off (*Phil. Trans.* (1814), 248ff.). Herschel attempted to classify, first, the ways in which stars are found associated with nebulosity, and, secondly, the various types of star clusters from the most irregular up to the beautiful globular aggregations into which he thought the Milky Way was destined eventually to resolve itself. His intention was to furnish additional evidence of the formation of stars by the condensation or absorption of nebulous material, and to illustrate from his own observations how stars once formed showed signs of drawing together into clusters, presumably under the 'clustering power' of their mutual attractions. 'It is one and the same power uniformly exerted which first condenses nebulous matter into stars, and afterwards draws them together into clusters, and which by a continuance of its action gradually increases the compression of the stars that form the clusters' (ibid., 271). Such 'clustering power' must, Herschel thought, eventually break the Milky Way up into globular clusters; and the gradual progress towards this final condition might serve to measure the slow passage of the ages as by a sort of celestial clock. We do not know the rate of the clock so as to reckon the time that is past; but 'since the breaking up of the parts of the Milky Way affords a proof that it cannot last for ever, it equally bears witness that its past duration cannot be admitted to be infinite' (ibid., 284).

6 A Conspectus

We have now completed our survey of Herschel's historic achievements in astronomy as they are set forth in the papers which he read from time to time to the Royal Society. It may be useful at this point to draw his discoveries and working-ideas into a brief synopsis before attempting, in a final chapter, to view them in the perspective of later developments of the science.

In his efforts to perfect the reflecting telescope Herschel bestowed more labour and expended more wealth than had probably ever been lavished before upon the development of any scientific instrument; and he acquired an immense experience in its use under all kinds of atmospheric conditions. He thereby established the reflector, not indeed as a fundamental but certainly as a capital instrument of the modern observatory. His name has become associated with the special type of reflector which he devised—the 'Herschelian'—in which the secondary mirror is eliminated and the incident light is reflected from the speculum directly into the eyepiece without further loss. Herschel also learned to distinguish between the several different functions which a telescope can perform, revealing stars invisible to the unaided eye, magnifying extended objects, and resolving close stellar pairs or clusters into separate images. And he clearly understood how these various capacities of a telescope depend upon the relevant optical dimensions of the instrument. Microscopy is a study on its own; and since Herschel's time there may be said to have existed a science of 'telescopy'. Herschel also stumbled upon and clearly described some of the small-scale optical phenomena of discs and fringes which we now attribute to the wave-structure of light but of which the accepted ideas of his day could afford no ready explanation. He was also fertile in the invention of optical adjuncts to the telescope, notably micrometers, and his technique for grinding and polishing short-focus lenses enabled him to employ magnifications of such powers as his contemporaries found barely credible.

Although Herschel is chiefly famed for his contributions to stellar and nebular astronomy, yet the majority of his papers relate to observations of the members of the solar system. His measurement of the heights of lunar mountains was an exercise in traditional telescopic astronomy. On the other hand his theory of the Sun's constitution, however physically ill founded, was the earliest serious attempt at a comprehensive, naturalistic explanation of the solar economy; and it created the *genre* of such theories, each of which persisted until superseded by a better one.

From the merely technical problem of devising a method for observing the Sun without injuring his eyesight, Herschel passed on to investigate the distribution of the heating-rays over the length of the solar spectrum. He established that the heating-effect increases towards the red end of the visible spectrum, that beyond the red end there are heating-rays (rising there to a maximum intensity) which do not affect the sense of sight, and that these rays obey the ordinary laws of reflection and refraction.

In the field of planetary astronomy it was Herschel's
outstanding achievement to have discovered, while still an
obscure amateur, the major planet which eventually received the name of Uranus; six years later he detected two
of the five satellites which this distant member of the solar
system is now known to possess. Herschel could make but
little of the inferior planets Mercury and Venus, the one
seldom to be observed except in the full glare of the Sun,
the other permanently shrouded in a mantle of cloud.
However, he was able to discredit the claims, both supported by the authority of Schröter, that Mercury possessed an atmosphere and Venus a mountainous landscape.
Herschel was among the first to grasp the possibility that
the Earth's rate of diurnal rotation might be suffering
diminution with lapse of time; he discussed such evidence
for that view as was forthcoming, and he pointed out the
effect that such a progressive change must have upon our
estimates of the speeds of other cosmic processes. He
determined the period of rotation of Mars within five
seconds of the figure accepted today; and he established
the fluctuations in the planet's white polar caps as seasonal
phenomena. Herschel did not discover any of the asteroids,
but he scrutinized the four of them detected by Continental
astronomers in his lifetime, and he established them as a
class under that name. He devoted particular attention to
the planet Saturn, discovering two of its satellites and
finding evidence of the planet's axial rotation, the period
of which he accurately estimated; he failed, however, to
divine the corpuscular nature of the rings. His studies on
the periodic variations of brightness in certain of the
satellites of Saturn and of Jupiter seemed to suggest that
these objects rotated in the same periods as those in which
they respectively revolved about their primary planets;
this condition (to which the Moon also conforms) might,
he supposed, have been gradually established by some sort

of gravitational leverage exerted by the planets upon their non-spherical satellites, all much in line with modern views on this phenomenon.

Herschel was an acute observer of the comets which swam into his ken from time to time, and he gave classic descriptions of what might be called the anatomy of the fully developed individual of this class of celestial objects. He grasped the role of what would now be called radiation pressure in the propagation of a comet's tail; and he sought compensation for the immense wastage which a comet suffers at its perihelion passage in an hypothesis anticipating in some degree the modern conception of a comet as a product of the accretion of interstellar material.

In the realm of stellar astronomy Herschel's contributions related to stars as individuals, as classes, as communities, and as evolutionary products. His authority gave support to the prevailing view that variable stars are rotating objects of non-spherical shape or of non-uniform surface brightness. As late as about 1865 J. C. F. Zöllner of Leipzig was experimenting with a model variable star in the form of a small globe unevenly shaded with light and dark chalks and illuminated by sunlight. He rotated the globe through fifteen degrees at a time, measuring its brightness in each position with a photometer some distance away and graphing the results as the light-curve of the model variable. By suitably distributing the bright and the dark areas on the globe he succeeded in realistically reproducing the fluctuations of a typical variable star. The hypothesis has retained its usefulness only as applied to account for the light-fluctuations of certain asteroids and planetary satellites of supposedly irregular shape. Herschel's procedure for detecting variables consisted in ordering a selected set of stars in a finely graduated sequence of ascending brightness and noting if any disturbances of the order occurred with lapse of time through the inconstancy of member stars. And his important contributions to the modern classification of the northern stars with respect to magnitude were communicated in catalogues constructed upon this principle.

Herschel's attempts to detect annual stellar parallax inevitably proved fruitless. The phenomenon sought must probably have escaped detection with his instruments; and in any case his procedure—the examination of close star-pairs of unequal brightness—was vitiated by the false assumption that the members of the pair must be at very different distances from the solar system. However, just as James Bradley's vain quest for the elusive parallax had led to his major discovery of the aberration of light, so Herschel's preoccupation with double stars, besides prompting the celestial reviews that revealed Uranus, enabled him eventually to establish the existence of true binary systems typified by a pair of stars revolving about a common centre of mass under their mutual gravitational attraction.

Working from insecure contemporary estimates of the proper motions of some dozen or so stars, Herschel made a bold attempt to determine the direction in which the Sun and its train of planets might be voyaging through space. As time went on more abundant data became available for analysis; and the conclusion to which these investigations consistently pointed has been broadly confirmed. Though necessarily starting out from the assumption that the individual motions of the stars show a random distribution, Herschel's researches revealed evidence of preferential stellar motions which tie up with modern theories of the 'local cluster' (of stars which share the Sun's proper motion) and the revolution of the stars about the galactic centre.

No problem was more suited to the genius of Herschel than that of delimiting and fathoming the system of the stars from an arbitrary station within its boundaries. He conceived the Galaxy as an optical effect resulting from the greater depth of stars through which our gaze passes in the galactic plane; and he employed his method of 'star-gaging' to estimate (with a minimum of simplifying assumptions) the extent of the stellar aggregation in every available direction. He catalogued the nebulae and star clusters; he discovered and named the so-called planetary nebulae, and he recognized an analogy between our stellar system and the nebulae supposedly external to it, which he at first conceived as telescopically resolvable into stars. His discovery of stars surrounded by luminous aureoles convinced him that the self-luminous material visible in the heavens was not all organized into stars but could exist in a dispersed condition, and that many irregular nebulae were constituted in this manner. In a final attack upon the problem of the Milky Way Herschel made trial of a more sophisticated technique involving a comparison of the brightness of stars, with inferences as to their relative distances; but he could never claim to have fathomed the galactic system of stars to its depths; and his conviction that it is a self-contained system, isolated in space from other such systems, remained something of an act of faith.

Herschel was among the first to conceive a celestial aggregation (for example a star cluster) as the product of a continuing process of formation which imprinted marks of age upon the developing system. And he grasped the important principle that any observation of a remote region of the Universe must relate to conditions prevailing there at a correspondingly remote period of time.

Chapter 6

Epilogue

In concluding this account of the labours of William Herschel it seems appropriate to say something about the progress of astronomy since his day, particularly in those branches of the science which he established or decisively influenced. Only a brief sketch can be attempted here of developments which make up a large part of the history of modern astronomy; and these will be considered in an order broadly corresponding to that adopted in the foregoing analysis of Herschel's papers.

The reflecting telescope, which Herschel did so much to improve and to establish, has continued to develop. The generation following his death saw the construction of what came to be known as 'Lord Rosse's telescope' after the Irish peer who wrought and erected it on his own estate at Parsonstown. The 6-foot mirror, polished by steam power, served to resolve many more nebulae into stars and to reveal for the first time the spiral structure which these objects frequently exhibit. In the latter part of the nineteenth century the metallic specula of the type fashioned by Herschel and Lord Rosse gradually gave place to mirrors of silvered glass; more recently, better reflection has been obtained by depositing aluminium on glass, fused quartz, or Pyrex. And during the past forty years telescopic penetration into interstellar space has been enormously extended, and the study of nebular forms greatly advanced, by means of the giant Hooker and Hale reflecting telescopes, of 100 inches and 200 inches aperture respectively, at the Mount Wilson and Palomar Observatories.

The predominant use of these instruments as huge cameras reminds us how, some fifty years after Herschel's death, astronomical techniques began to be transformed through the introduction of celestial photography. The astronomer's son played a vital part in the invention of the photographic process as we know it. By choosing a time when the atmospheric conditions are excellent and the selected celestial object well placed in the sky, and exposing a sensitive plate upon it for a few minutes, or hours, an exact permanent and unbiased record is obtained of the object's appearance, capable of rapid multiplication, such as might otherwise have consumed weeks of an astronomical draughtsman's observing time. And since the action of light upon the plate is cumulative, it is possible, by lengthening the exposure, to record features too faint for the eye to perceive even with the largest telescope.

None of Herschel's views proved more completely mistaken than those he entertained as to the constitution of the Sun. The phenomena which were decisively to disprove his solar theory were already known in his day; but their significance was only slowly grasped as sounder ideas took shape on the relations of heat, energy, and radiation. About 1814 Joseph Fraunhofer, while examining the spectrum of sunlight admitted through a narrow slit, noticed that the coloured band was crossed by numerous dark lines indicating the absence of certain coloured constituents from the light. As the century drew on, it became established that every chemical substance, when heated to incandescence, gives a characteristic spectrum of bright lines which constitutes a test of its presence. The technique of spectrum analysis was securely founded by R. W.

Bunsen and G. R. Kirchhoff, who gave the spectroscope the standard form familiar in our laboratories today. In 1859 Kirchhoff announced his discovery that light passing through an incandescent vapour suffers a selective absorption of those constituents which correspond to the bright lines in the spectrum of the vapour. He established that many of the dark lines of the solar spectrum coincided in position with bright lines in the spectra of common chemical elements; he interpreted the solar lines as due to absorption and argued the presence of these elements in the Sun's atmosphere. He was thus led to picture the Sun as consisting of an intensely hot solid or liquid core surrounded by a layer of cooler but still incandescent gases. And that, broadly speaking, is how the Sun is still conceived, though now as a gaseous body throughout. The spectroscopic study of the Sun's structure was begun by J. Norman Lockyer and greatly advanced by G. E. Hale.

Herschel was aware that more sunspots had been observed in some years than in others; and in 1826 Heinrich Schwabe of Dessau started his daily count of spot groups which, continued through many years, eventually established that the annual totals show a regular fluctuation having a period of ten or eleven years. A corresponding periodicity was soon afterwards discovered in the principal phenomena of terrestrial magnetism. Meanwhile it was shown that the solar latitudes for which sunspots exhibit a statistical preference change progressively in the course of each spot cycle, and that the Sun does not rotate like a rigid body: spots on the solar equator complete a revolution about two days before those situated half-way towards the poles of the Sun. Sunspots are no longer regarded as openings in a luminous envelope revealing a dark surface within. A typical sunspot is a cooler patch upon the Sun's brilliant surface, dark only by contrast, sometimes slightly depressed below the surrounding surface; it is the centre of a gaseous circulation and of an intense magnetic field produced by the whirlpool motions of ions (electrically charged particles), which act like a current flowing in an electromagnet and which modify in a characteristic manner the spectrum of the light coming to us from the spot. There is still no universally accepted explanation of how sunspots originate. A characteristic solar phenomenon is the occurrence of a related pair of spots exhibiting opposite magnetic polarities; and one typical theory postulates the existence of cylindrical vortices underlying the Sun's surface. Wherever such a vortex intersects the surface such a spot pair will appear.

Herschel was one of the first to speculate (in accordance with the scientific ideas of his day) as to how the Sun's output of light is maintained. He suggested that the wastage of luminous material might be made good by the accession of cometary vapours. An hypothesis related to the sounder views which were taking shape on the mutual convertibility of heat and 'motion' was that put forward in 1848 by J. R. Mayer, who supposed that the Sun's heat was generated by the impact of meteors falling upon its surface. This theory was given a rather different form in 1854 by H. von Helmholtz. He supposed that the Sun, in the course of the ages, suffers a slow contraction, the gravitational energy thereby lost reappearing as heat. By the beginning of the present century the source of solar (and stellar) energy had come to be vaguely identified with some radioactive or other atomic transformation; but for the past twenty-five years the theory has generally prevailed that the radiation of the celestial luminaries is maintained by thermo-nuclear processes occurring in their interiors and (in stars like the Sun) involving the conversion of hydrogen into helium with the production of a surplus of energy for radiation into space.

Contemporary with Lockyer in the pioneer study of the

Sun's atmosphere was William Huggins. He introduced a spectroscopic method for estimating the relative speed of a celestial object in the observer's line of sight, which, although originally applied to determining the motions of bright stars, has yet found so many other applications in astronomy that it had best be mentioned here. Huggins used a principle formulated by Christian Doppler in 1842. If an observer analyses the light from a luminous source into a spectrum, any relative motion of source and observer along the line joining them causes the spectral lines to be displaced from the positions they would occupy if the two were in relative rest (as indicated by the spectrum of a stationary source in the laboratory). If the motion be such as to lessen the distance between source and observer, the displacement is towards the violet; if otherwise, towards the red. The measurement of such 'Doppler effects' enables the relative speed of source and observer to be estimated e.g. in kilometres a second. Many applications of Doppler's Principle have been made in astronomy. The Sun's rate of rotation in various solar latitudes has been deduced from the relative displacement of two spectra formed by beams of light coming from opposite edges of the solar disc, the one approaching and the other receding from the observer. The same technique has been applied to the planets. The Doppler effect has served also for the measurement of the speeds, in the line of sight, of the luminous material composing the outer layers of the Sun, the so-called prominences, and for exploring the flow of gases in the neighbourhood of sunspots.

The astronomy of the solar system has made notable advances since Herschel's day. The Italian observer G. V. Schiaparelli, after keeping watch for years upon the faint surface markings of Mercury, had established by 1889 that the elusive planet's period of axial rotation—its 'day'— equals its period of revolution about the Sun—its 'year'.

It must therefore always turn the same face (very nearly) towards the Sun, just as the Moon does towards the Earth, the tides raised by the Sun on the planet having presumably operated to bring the two periods into equality. On the other hand the period of rotation of the outwardly featureless planet Venus remains unknown, though spectroscopic analysis of light reflected from its cloud-laden atmosphere has revealed the presence of carbon dioxide.

A gradual slowing down of the Earth's axial rotation through the ages, suspected by Herschel, is now admitted; and a convincing explanation has been found in the friction of the ocean tides, particularly of tidal currents in shallow waters. There occur also minute discontinuous changes in the length of the day, probably caused by redistributions of matter within the Earth, which must, on mechanical principles, give rise to corresponding 'jumps' in the Earth's rate of rotation. Whatever the deficiencies of the timepieces of Herschel's day, astronomers now have at their disposal clocks controlled by the electrically maintained vibrations of quartz crystals, which go steadily enough to show up the more pronounced discontinuities as they occur.

The conspicuous surface markings on the planet Mars have continued to attract attention; and the existence of a Martian atmosphere dense enough to support clouds has been confirmed. Sir John Herschel lent his authority to the view that the ruddy areas represented land, probably red sandstone, while the bluish patches were seas; but these latter regions, which exhibit seasonal changes, are now thought to support some form of vegetation, probably analogous to our terrestrial lichens. Scrutinizing Mars at its opposition of 1877, Schiaparelli saw the planetary disc scored with intersecting lines which came to be called the 'canals'. Percival Lowell elaborated a theory of artificial watercourses constructed by the Martians for the irrigation of their partly desiccated planet; but the conviction has grown that the phenomenon is of the nature of an optical illusion. At the same historic opposition of 1877 a pair of Martian satellites, too minute for Herschel's telescopes to reveal, were discovered by Asaph Hall of Washington.

Asteroids, so named and constituted as a class by Herschel, were discovered in increasing numbers as the nineteenth century passed, particularly following the application by Max Wolf of Heidelberg in 1891 of a photographic technique for seeking out these unobtrusive members of the solar system. Olbers's hypothesis of the origin of the asteroids from the disruption of a quondam major planet has continued to excite discussion.

Herschel's estimate of the period of rotation of Saturn has been confirmed, and two more satellites of the planet have been discovered. The long-standing riddle of the nature of Saturn's ring was cleared up in 1857 when James Clerk Maxwell established that the ring must consist of a vast cloud of small satellites revolving round the planet in independent orbits. About forty years later, in 1895, Maxwell's conclusion received striking confirmation from spectroscopic observations of the rings carried out by the American astronomer J. E. Keeler, who studied the Doppler effects exhibited by the various parts of the Saturnian system. If any one of the rings were a solid body revolving in one piece, the outer edge would have to travel at a greater speed than the inner edge. If however it is composed of minute satellites, then the greater their distances from the planet the less will be their speeds, in accordance with the laws of satellite motion. When the slit of the spectroscope was placed equatorially across a telescopic image of the planet and its rings, the observed Doppler displacements were in accordance with the latter supposition and not with the former, the rings being thus divided into satellites.

Plate 20   Globular star cluster in Hercules.

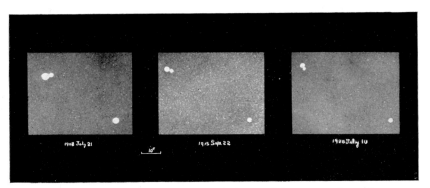

Plate 21   The system Krueger 60, photographed on 21 July 1908, 22 September 1915, and 10 July 1920, showing progressive orbital motion in the pair of stars in the top left-hand corner.

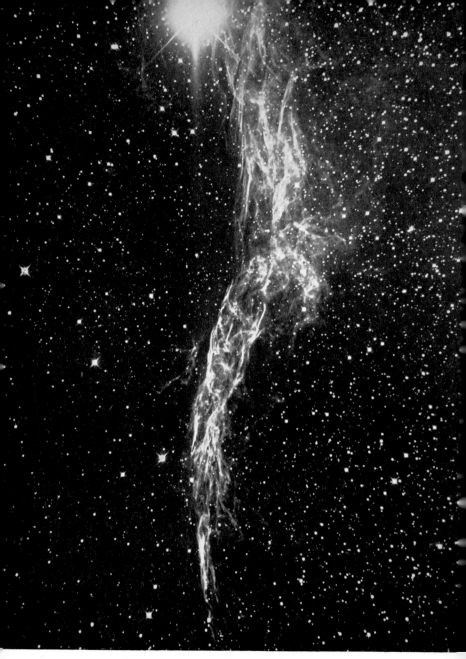

Plate 22 Filamentary nebula in Cygnus (a galactic nebula).

Three more satellites of Uranus have been discovered since Herschel's time, making five in all; and the planet's period of rotation has been determined spectroscopically. Following the discovery of Uranus in 1781, search was made through old records for any earlier determinations of the planet's position, and it transpired that on nearly a score of occasions (the earliest an observation by Flamsteed in 1690) note had been taken of the object, always under the impression that it was a star. In preparing the tables of the motion of Uranus which he published in 1821, Alexis Bouvard expected to find these old observations of great assistance as enabling him to follow the course of the planet (whose period of revolution is 84 years) right round its orbit. However, he found that they could not be combined into a single theory with the observations made since 1781, so he set them aside and based his tables on these more recent data with the remark that the discrepancies might be the result of the disturbing action of some unknown planet. But as the years passed, growing divergencies showed themselves between the observed and the tabular places of the planet. By 1835 the calculated longitudes of Uranus differed from the observed ones by 30 seconds of arc; in 1838 the discrepancy amounted to 50 seconds and in 1841 to 70 seconds. The calculated distances of the planet from the Sun were also found to be considerably in error. The hypothesis of an unknown disturbing planet gained growing acceptance; and the problem presented itself: from the known disturbances of Uranus in known positions, to deduce the unknown position of the disturbing planet at a given time. The great German mathematician F. W. Bessel, while on a visit to England in 1842, announced to Sir John Herschel his intention of tackling the problem; but his untimely death brought this project to naught. Meanwhile two young mathematicians, J. C. Adams and U. J. J. Leverrier, the one British and the

K

other French, had addressed themselves to the investigation. Their calculations enabled them independently to pinpoint the position of a disturbing planet exterior to Uranus and responsible for upsetting its motion. On 23 September 1846 J. G. Galle of the Berlin Observatory received the vital information from Leverrier, and he discovered the planet the same night: it received the name of Neptune.

A further analysis by Percival Lowell of residual disturbances of the motion of Uranus (not attributable to the attraction of any known planet) led in 1930 to the discovery by photography of the planet Pluto, the outermost known planetary member of the Sun's train. This was the achievement of Mr Clyde W. Tombaugh, a young farmer and keen amateur astronomer working at the observatory which Lowell had founded in Arizona. The fact that Pluto seems not to possess sufficient mass to perturb Uranus to the extent observed suggests that it may prove to be the first of a series of small planets of the 'terrestrial' type revolving in orbits beyond Neptune.

We still distinguish with Herschel the four characteristic features normally, though not invariably, present in a comet, the diffuse coma, the star-like nucleus (forming with the coma the head of the comet), the envelopes, or shells, sometimes thrown off at intervals by a cometary head on its sunward side, and the spectacular tail. The more searching scrutiny of these visitants made possible by photography has confirmed Herschel's account of the rapid and characteristic metamorphoses which they undergo on approaching the Sun, and which render it impossible to establish a comet's identity between successive returns to our sky except by reference to the elements which specify its orbit.

Comets have come to be regarded as swarms of particles of various sizes accompanied by dust and gas. The force repelling from the Sun the particles composing a comet's tail, conceived by H. Olbers as an electrical repulsion, is now identified (in broad conformity to Herschel's views) with the experimentally established radiation pressure of the Sun's beams. In the seventies of the last century the Russian astronomer T. A. Bredichin tried to interpret the configuration of a comet's tail as the course of a particle moving under the combined forces of a gravitational attraction and of some form of repulsion, both residing in the Sun and standing in a certain ratio which he sought to determine. Comets show a propensity to form several tails, differing in length and in curvature, which should correspond to different values of this ratio; and Bredichin thought they might be composed of different chemical substances. More recent studies, employing spectroscopic techniques, have revealed the complexity of the physical processes occurring in comets under solar excitation. The spectroscope was not available to Herschel as a tool for investigating the nature of comets. Its use for this purpose, beginning with Donati in 1864, has revealed, in comets sufficiently bright, the spectrum of reflected sunlight and, superimposed upon this, the bright bands characteristic of hydrocarbon molecules under some form of excitation. Comets approaching sufficiently near to the Sun also exhibit lines indicative of the presence of metals, particularly of sodium.

Herschel was twenty years of age when, towards the end of 1758, Halley's comet made its predicted return. A year after his death J. F. Encke established the existence of a second periodic comet which passes round the Sun once in about three and a third years: it is typical of many inconspicuous short-period comets since discovered. Such objects, returning to the Sun every few years, often follow elliptic paths extending outward about as far as the orbit of Jupiter and intersecting the Jovian orbital plane in the very track of the planet. It is natural to regard these comets as having been 'captured' for the solar system by the attraction of the Sun's most massive planet, a theory foreshadowed by Laplace and elaborated towards the close of the nineteenth century. Other 'families' of comets have been associated, on evidence that carries less conviction, with the remaining giant planets. Arguing against this 'capture theory', R. A. Proctor preferred to regard the comets forming Jupiter's 'family' as composed of material thrown off by the developing planet in the course of eruptions similar to those observed on the Sun. The origin of comets has, however, remained down to our own day a field for ingenious speculation. Neither Proctor's hypothesis nor the related one, that comets originate as solar prominences, possesses any foundation either in observation or in theory. Serious objections have also been urged against regarding comets as originating from debris left over after the formation of the planets, or as produced by the disruption of asteroids which ventured so close to giant planets as to be broken to pieces by the tidal forces exerted upon them by the latter. Herschel, as we saw, tentatively conceived comets as recruiting their substance at the expense of nebulae through which they pass. His suggestion invites comparison with the theory, elaborated in recent years by the so-called 'New Cosmologists', that comets are formed by accretion of interstellar dust under the Sun's gravitational attraction (see R. A Lyttleton, *The Comets and their Origin*, Cambridge, 1953).

The theory starts out from the established existence in interstellar space of vast clouds of dust, a product perhaps of the stellar explosions which give rise to the super-novae, temporary stars of exceptional brilliance appearing at infrequent intervals. The Sun, in the course of its hypothetical revolution round the centre of the galactic system, may be supposed to pass through such clouds from time to time.

The effect of the Sun's gravitational attraction upon any dust particle within its range is to pull the particle in towards the Sun's wake, where it is likely to collide with and bring to a halt some other particle moving in the opposite direction. In this way a filament of matter is built up along the track already traversed by the Sun, the so-called accretion axis. Under the mutual attractions of its parts this filament breaks up into segments; and those segments which are formed within a certain critical distance of the Sun move towards it. Some of them are saved from actually falling into the Sun by the perturbing action of the planets, particularly of Jupiter; and they start revolving round the Sun as comets. The passage of a comet through its perihelion (the point of its orbit nearest to the Sun) must be accompanied by numerous collisions between components of the comet travelling in slightly different orbital planes. The particles of dust thereby produced are available (within certain limits of size) for the formation of a cometary tail under the Sun's radiation pressure; and they may be compared to the 'unperihelioned matter' of Herschel's hypothesis.

The systematic study of variable stars was taken up about twenty years after Herschel's death; later, photographic, photometric, and spectroscopic methods were used in seeking for these objects, which are known to run into thousands. The earliest workers in this field followed his original technique of regularly comparing a suspected variable with a sequence of neighbouring stars; these were selected so as to constitute a fixed, graduated scale of brightness against which any fluctuations in the luminosity of the suspect soon showed itself. The obvious photographic procedure, introduced later by the Harvard astronomer E. C. Pickering, was to expose two plates upon a selected field of stars with an interval of several days between the exposures, and then to compare the two negatives with an eye to telltale differences in intensity between corresponding images of the same star. The detection of such differences between the negatives was in due course facilitated by the introduction of ingenious optical devices. It was at Harvard, again, that a technique was developed for the spectroscopic diagnosis of long-period variable stars such as Mira Ceti, which had furnished the theme of Herschel's earliest contribution to the Royal Society. Their spectra are wont to exhibit bright lines which appear and fade periodically with the same rhythm as the light-fluctuations of the star. During the past hundred years increasing use has been made of stellar photometers—instruments for measuring the apparent brightness of stars—both for the determination of magnitudes and for the detection of variables. The simplest form of the instrument consisted essentially of a thin wedge of tinted glass which could be slowly drawn across the observer's field of vision as he viewed the star through his telescope. The relative brightness of two stars could be determined by finding what thicknesses of the glass must be interposed in order to extinguish each star image in turn. In other stellar photometers a star was compared with an artificial point source of light, a polarizing device serving to reduce the brighter of the two images in a measured proportion so as to bring it into equality with the fainter. More refined and sophisticated photometers, introduced during the present century, depend upon photoelectric phenomena, governed by numerical relations between the intensity of the incident light and the flow of electric current thereby produced.

Regular fluctuations in the brightness of a star were sometimes explained in Herschel's day by supposing it to possess a dark satellite which in the course of its revolution was periodically interposed between us and the bright star, thereby shutting off some of its light. This is still the accepted explanation for one type of variable star, not strictly a 'variable' at all but an 'eclipsing binary' system in whose common orbital plane the observer chances to be situated (Fig. 13). Herschel's own favourite conception, of a rotating globe not uniformly bright all over, persisted well into the nineteenth century. Alternatively, following the discovery of sunspot periodicity, the Sun was sometimes conceived as a typical variable star, its period of variability being that of the eleven-year sunspot cycle. Whether

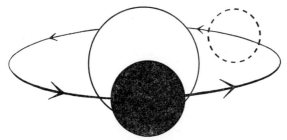

Fig. 13 A dark star revolving round a bright star periodically shuts off some of the light of the latter from an observer situated in the orbital plane of the system.

the maximum brightness should be taken to coincide with the maximum or with the minimum of sunspot activity was a matter of dispute. Later nineteenth-century theories of variable stars referred to the heating-effects supposed to be periodically excited between two stars or meteor swarms revolving round a common mass-centre and grazing as they passed nearest to each other. For fifty years now variable stars have been widely regarded as pulsating spheres of gas alternately expanding and contracting under opposing forces of gravity and internal radiation pressure. Their peculiar behaviour has been related to the theory that stellar radiation is maintained by thermo-nuclear processes which have the property of being accelerated by any increase in the internal temperature of the star. The several distinct types of variability

found among the cooler stars have been tentatively related to the several kinds of nuclear fuel consumed by these
luminaries.

It is interesting to plot the day-by-day apparent brightness of a variable star against the lapse of time, so obtaining a graph called the *light curve* of the star (Fig. 14).
Variable stars can be classified according to the types of
light curve which they exhibit; and one important class of
these objects is that of the Cepheids, so called after the star

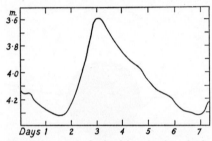

Fig. 14 The light curve obtained by plotting the brightness
of the star Delta Cephei in magnitudes against the lapse of
time in days.

Delta Cephei, a typical member of the class. Their
periodicity is marked by great regularity; the brightness
rises rapidly to a maximum and declines more slowly; and
the period varies from star to star, ranging from a few
hours to many days. About fifty years ago it was discovered (by Henrietta S. Leavitt of Harvard) that there
exists a simple mathematical relation connecting the
period of a Cepheid with its 'absolute' magnitude (its
magnitude as it would appear if viewed from some standard distance). When this relation had been determined
numerically it became possible, wherever in the heavens a
Cepheid is observed, to ascertain its period and thence to
calculate its absolute magnitude. But the difference between the absolute magnitude of a star and its (easily
measurable) apparent magnitude gives an indication of its

distance from the observer; and hence the way was opened to finding the distance of any star whose light curve shows it to be a Cepheid. Now Cepheids abound in star clusters and in nebulae; in fact it was the investigation of the Cepheids in the nebula called the Lesser Magellanic Cloud (which could all be regarded as being at roughly equal distances from our system) that led to the discovery of 'Leavitt's Law'. They therefore serve as convenient sounding-lines for plumbing the depths of space and determining the distances of the various stellar aggregations in which they occur.

The development of stellar photometry owed much to the astronomer's son Sir John Herschel. Using a simple type of photometer he estimated that an average star of the first magnitude is about one hundred times as bright as one of the sixth magnitude; and he established that the equal gradations of apparent brightness from each magnitude to the next correspond to a constant *ratio* of luminosity. This was in accordance with Fechner's psychophysical law that when the intensity of a stimulus increases in geometrical progression the nervous sensation produced increases in arithmetical progression. It was upon this foundation that N. R. Pogson of Oxford based the modern scientific system of stellar photometry. With the introduction of photography there was to arise an independent system of photographic magnitudes, differing from the visual ones but similarly organized.

Sixteen years after Herschel's death a new era in stellar astronomy was begun by F. W. Bessel, who was the first to publish an authentic determination of the distance of a star from the solar system. Bessel adopted the procedure which Herschel had recommended, and measured the differential parallax between stars appearing close to one another in the sky but situated (there was reason to suppose) at very different distances from the Sun. In his endeavour to select for examination a near star neighbour such as *ought* to exhibit a measurable parallax, Bessel was guided not by the brightness of the object but by its conspicuous proper motion across the general background of the constellations. His choice fell upon a faint star in the constellation of the Swan known as 61 Cygni; it is not bright enough to merit identification by a Greek letter but it possesses proper motion in a marked degree (about 5·2 seconds of arc a year). For many months he measured its angular distances from two neighbouring faint stars known to be changing their positions in the sky so slowly as to suggest that they might be too remote from us to exhibit parallaxes comparable to that of 61 Cygni. The measurements were carried out by means of a heliometer, a type of micrometer developed by the eighteenth-century optician John Dollond and intended primarily for determining with great precision the apparent breadth of the Sun's disc. Bessel's results indicated an annual parallax of about one-third of a second of arc for 61 Cygni, corresponding to a distance of the order of sixty million million miles. It subsequently appeared that Bessel had been anticipated in his establishment of a stellar parallax by Thomas Henderson, Astronomer Royal for Scotland, whose results, however, referred to the bright southern star Alpha Centauri: during his period of service at the Cape Observatory he had regularly determined the altitude at which the star transits across the meridian, and from an analysis of the fluctuations in these measurements he was able to conclude that Alpha Centauri is about twenty-five million million miles away. The star forms a member of a triple system believed to be the Sun's nearest celestial neighbours. However, Bessel's announcement was published before Henderson's and the priority went to the German astronomer.

The measurements involved in direct determinations of

parallax were subsequently rendered more precise and less exacting by the introduction of photography; but only relatively few stars are near enough to us to exhibit a measurable parallax. However, indirect methods, some of them depending upon spectroscopic observations or upon determinations of stellar brightness, have become available. Most of them give results indicating only the average distances of *classes* of stars; but the important point is that estimates of stellar and nebular distances are available to astronomers such as were quite unobtainable in Herschel's day. The apparent brightness to our eyes of a star depends partly upon how bright it is in itself and partly upon how near it is to us. We now know that stars differ largely both in intrinsic brightness and in distance, and that Herschel went far astray in assuming, even if only as a simplifying hypothesis, that the stars were all of roughly the same brightness in themselves.

The double-star measurements of Herschel and Struve have been repeated and extended to include many thousands of these objects. Short-period doubles which no telescope can resolve are often detected through a periodic doubling of the spectral lines as one member star moves away and the other approaches the observer, another example of the Doppler effect. From the orbital elements of binary systems (deduced from their apparent orbits as projected upon the sky) it is possible in certain instances to obtain authentic information about the masses of the member stars (cf. Pl. 21); the results tend to the conclusion that the masses of stars (unlike their intrinsic luminosities) are generally of the same order as that of the Sun, though the sizes and densities vary within vastly wider limits.

No *direct* measurements have been made of the size of a star. Even the most powerful modern telescopes do not show, and none is ever likely to show, a star as a disc of measurable breadth. But the angular diameters of several of the largest stars have been determined by an indirect method depending upon the peculiar properties of light. Herschel accepted during his formative years, and apparently retained to the end of his days, a long-established view as to the nature of light, believed at that period to be supported by the authority of Newton. According to this hypothesis a beam of light consisted of a stream of particles which were continually emitted by the luminous source and which travelled in straight lines until they encountered some opaque obstacle. However, about the beginning of the nineteenth century this 'corpuscular hypothesis' began to be superseded by a rival conception of light as consisting of waves propagated from a luminous body and travelling outward through an aether filling all space. When Herschel died this latter view had become generally accepted, and it still suffices for describing the behaviour of light at the elementary level, though for an explanation of the more recondite phenomena physicists have had recourse to a conception partaking in some measure of the corpuscular hypothesis. Now a wave theory of light implies and is intended to explain, certain small-scale optical effects which Herschel encountered when he tried to measure minute planetary discs or to set his micrometer wires upon barely separable pairs of stars. These effects arise because light waves, like waves of water in a pond, can be made to interact so as to destroy one another and give no disturbance—no light—at all. This principle, first grasped by Thomas Young, serves to explain why, as has already been mentioned, a star image viewed in the field of the telescope appears as a minute central disc surrounded by alternate bright and dark rings. This phenomenon has been exploited by the so-called interferometer, designed to measure the separation of close stellar pairs and the angular diameters of selected stars.

If the object glass or the reflecting mirror of a telescope

be covered with an opaque screen having two small openings on the same diameter, equally and oppositely distant from the centre, each opening will produce its own disc at the point where the lens or mirror would form the image of the star. The two beams of light, by their mutual interference, produce a fringe of bright and dark lines; these lines are closer together in proportion as the openings in the screen are more widely separated. The interferometer is just such a device designed for attachment to a telescope and equipped for varying and accurately measuring the separation of its two openings and for rotating them round the axis of the instrument. It serves primarily for measuring the angular separation of a close pair of stars, each member of which will produce its own set of bright and dark lines without interference between the two sets, since the light comes from different sources. The apparatus can be set so that the bright lines of one system fall on the dark lines of the other; and by finding the least separation of the slits which will effect this, and making some assumption as to the mean wavelength of the light forming the fringes, it is possible to calculate the angular separation of the stellar pair.

However, the application of the interferometer which chiefly concerns us here relates to the measurement of the angular diameters of stars. For this purpose the two halves of a star's disc must be thought of as corresponding to the two components of a close double star; and in fact they behave as if all their light was concentrated at equal and calculable distances on each side of the centre of the disc. The classic application of this technique (following earlier pioneer ventures) was that effected with an interferometer designed by A. A. Michelson for application to the 100-inch telescope at Mount Wilson and employed by the astronomer F. G. Pease in 1920 to measure the angular diameter of the giant star Betelgeuse: on a probable esti-

mate of the star's distance this must correspond to a
diameter of about 250,000,000 miles: if the star were
centred upon the Sun its surface would extend outward
nearly as far as the orbit of Mars. The gases composing
the outer envelope of such an object must be rarefied to a
degree beyond that of any vacuum which can be artificially
produced in our laboratories. At the other extreme are the
stars known as 'white dwarfs'; they are typified by the
companion star of Sirius which, although barely less
massive than the Sun, has suffered compression until its
radius is only about three times that of the Earth.

Herschel's conclusions as to the direction in which the
Sun is voyaging through space were at first received with
incredulity even by his own son. But later determinations
of the apex, based upon analyses of the proper motions of
more numerous assortments of stars, or employing spectroscopic techniques not available to him, have generally
confirmed Herschel's findings; though many considerations
which did not trouble him have since arisen to complicate
the problem for us.

Huggins had shown how to measure the velocities of
stars in the line of sight, utilizing the Doppler effect: this
affords an independent approach to Herschel's problem.
The stars in that half of the sky towards which the Sun is
moving should (on the average) appear to be approaching
us, and the more rapidly the nearer they are to the apex
of the Sun's way. This method (of which classic application was made by W. W. Campbell of the Lick Observatory at the beginning of the present century) has the advantage that it does not involve waiting for proper motions
to become measurable with the lapse of time; and it yields
not only the direction but also the speed of the Sun's travel,
about twenty kilometres a second.

The task of determining the contour and dimensions of
our stellar system was again taken up and pursued in the

century following Herschel's death, notably by H. von
Seeliger and J. C. Kapteyn, employing more elaborate
statistical procedures and taking account of the great
diversity in the intrinsic brightness of stars. Like Herschel
and John Michell, Kapteyn sought information as to the
extent of the stellar system by merely counting the number
of stars brighter than a certain magnitude and finding how
this number varied according to the limit of magnitude
and the region of the heavens selected. Out of his researches,
latterly pursued in collaboration with P. J. van Rhijn, there
emerged about 1920 the conception of the 'Kapteyn
Universe', a vast spheroidal cloud of stars, all revolving
round the short axis of the spheroid with the Sun situated
not far from the central point. The 'rotation of the Galaxy'
linked up with Kapteyn's earlier discovery of the preference which the stars exhibit for moving towards one
or other of two opposite points on the celestial sphere.
This phenomenon rendered inadmissible the assumption
that the proper motions of the stars are random (apart
from the effects of the solar motion). An alternative
approach to the problem of the figure of the galactic
system was attempted by Professor Harlow Shapley,
following his study, commenced in 1914, of the distribution in space of the globular clusters. There was reason
to suppose that the stars of our system were arranged
symmetrically about the same centre as the clusters; and
Shapley came to regard the system as having the shape of
a watch, with the stars and clusters grouped symmetrically
round the common axis of the hour and minute hands,
while the Sun's position, some way from the centre, was
indicated by the axis of the second hand.

The spectra of stars, to which Herschel devoted but a
passing glance, began to be seriously investigated by
William Huggins in 1862, following Kirchhoff's work on
the solar spectrum. He established the presence of terres-

trially known elements in the stars and attempted the earliest classification of stellar spectra, the graduated, one-track series of spectral types suggesting an evolutionary sequence through which a star might pass. More elaborate classifications have followed: at first they were thought to support the theory, generally consonant with Herschel's conclusions, that a star begins its career intensely hot and gradually cools down through red heat to extinction. This view gave place in the eighties to Lockyer's hypothesis that a star began its career as a relatively cool body (or meteor swarm), subsequently rising, through increasing condensation, to a maximum temperature and then cooling down again. For the last forty years theories of stellar evolution have been in the melting-pot.

A fundamentally important development in astronomy since Herschel's time has been the separation of the objects which he broadly designated as nebulae into two separate classes differing vastly in cosmic status. Even Herschel, as we saw, came to distinguish between nebulae which are essentially collections of stars and those which must be regarded as composed of a 'shining fluid' or, as we should say, of incandescent gas. The latter class of objects, bright, irregular clouds and planetary nebulae, show a preference for the plane of the Milky Way and, on that account, came to be called *galactic nebulae* (Pl. 22). The former class, as Herschel pointed out, appear to avoid the plane of the Milky Way and to crowd towards its poles; and for that reason they were called *extra-galactic nebulae* (Pls. 23, 24). But during the past forty years or so these terms have taken on a deeper significance as indicating that the diffuse clouds and planetaries belong to the galactic system of stars of which the Sun is a member, while stellar aggregations are extra-galactic in the further sense of being completely independent of the galactic system and comparable to it in status.

Plate 23   The great nebula in Andromeda (an extra-galactic nebula).

Plate 24   Part of the great nebula in Andromeda, showing resolution
into stars.

Conclusive evidence of the distinction between these two classes of objects was first afforded by the spectroscope. On the evening of 29 August 1864 William Huggins directed his spectroscope to a nebula in the constellation Draco; he observed a bright-line spectrum and thus established the gaseous composition of the nebula. Of some seventy such objects which he subsequently examined in this manner, about one-third, including the great nebula in Orion, gave spectra of the gaseous type; the others, among them the great nebula in Andromeda, gave absorption spectra showing them to be composed, at least in part, of stars. Many members of this latter class, when viewed through Lord Rosse's telescope, had been found to exhibit a spiral structure. There seemed to be an analogy between these spiral, stellar aggregations and the galactic system of stars of which the Sun is a member, tending to support Herschel's surmise that the distant nebulae which he glimpsed were 'universes' like ours. And that is the view that has come to be taken of them within the last forty years or so.

It was E. P. Hubble and his colleagues at the Mount Wilson Observatory who played the decisive part in establishing the status of the extra-galactic nebulae as external universes and in clarifying their constitution, morphology, evolutionary history, and distribution. It was found that the majority of these objects could be grouped into classes which are thought to represent an evolutionary sequence. First come the elliptical nebulae, without a spiral structure but ranging in appearance from discs to spindle-shaped forms according to their degree of flattening and the angle at which we view them. They merge into the characteristic spiral nebulae, which immediately divide into two parallel sequences according as the two spiral arms spring directly from the nucleus or from the opposite ends of a transverse bar. Transition from class to

L

class along either sequence goes with a progressive
growth and opening out of the arms at the expense of the
nucleus, and with the formation of condensations and stars
in the nebular material.

The final decision as to the status of these objects depended upon the detection in the nebulae of special types
of stars, including Cepheids, whose intrinsic brightness,
and hence their distances from us (and those of the parent
nebulae), could be estimated. The marked tendency of
what are now loosely called the spiral nebulae to avoid
the plane of the Milky Way had impressed Herschel; and
it long constituted a serious argument against the view
that these objects are wholly independent of the galactic
system of stars and equal in status to it. However, Hubble
was able to explain this phenomenon on the ground that
many nebulae of this kind, situated in the galactic plane,
must be hidden from us by the opaque or absorbent
material abounding therein. This material masks whatever lies behind it; and that explains Herschel's observation that galactic nebulae are frequently found interspersed
with starless patches of sky. He had noted also the tendency for diffuse nebulae to occur near bright stars; and
this is no accident, for such nebulae depend for their
luminosity upon star neighbours. Either they reflect the
stars' light from the dust and frozen droplets of which they
partly consist, or, if the stellar radiation is sufficiently intense, it excites the nebular gases to radiate on their own
account, with the production of the characteristic bright-
line spectrum.

The distribution of the external nebulae through space
has been investigated by the same sort of procedure as that
adopted for the stars by Michell, Herschel, and Kapteyn,
namely, by counting and locating on the sphere all nebulae
brighter than a certain limit and then finding how the
count increases as the limit is lowered by one magnitude

at a time. The general result was that the distribution of these objects is broadly uniform over the sky and in space to the depth reached by the great American telescopes. The spectra of these remote nebulae exhibit displacements which, regarded as Doppler effects, suggest that the nebulae are receding into space with speeds proportional to their distances from the observer. The resulting 'expansion of the Universe' has been interpreted with reference to the theory of relativity in physics. More remote depths of space have been plumbed by the special 'telescopes' designed for the purpose of detecting radio emissions coming to us from cosmic sources; and information so obtained is widely held to throw light upon the origins of the physical Universe. And this must conclude our attempt to map some of the paths, opened or signposted by William Herschel, along which astronomers have fared during the past century and a half to attain heights and to survey horizons transcending his boldest imaginations.

L *

Bibliography

Herschel's classic papers were published in the *Philosophical Transactions of the Royal Society* during the years 1780 to 1818 and (his last paper) in the *Memoirs of the* (Royal) *Astronomical Society*, Vol. 1 (1822), 166ff.

They were reproduced, with much additional material, in *The Scientific Papers of Sir William Herschel* (2 vols., London, 1912). Their contents were summarized by E. S. Holden and C. S. Hastings in 'A Synopsis of the Scientific Writings of Sir William Herschel' (Smithsonian Report for 1880, 509ff.).

The authoritative source for the life story of William and Caroline Herschel is Constance A. Lubbock, *The Herschel Chronicle* (Cambridge, 1933).

The following books also deal with the life and work of Herschel from various points of view:

Mrs John Herschel, *Memoir and Correspondence of Caroline Herschel* (London, 1876)

E. S. Holden, *Sir William Herschel: His Life and Works* (New York, 1881)

Agnes M. Clerke, *The Herschels and Modern Astronomy* (London, 1895)

J. Sime, *William Herschel and His Work* (Edinburgh, 1900)

H. Macpherson, *Herschel* (London, 1919)

J. B. Sidgwick, *William Herschel: Explorer of the Heavens* (London, 1953)

M. A. Hoskin, *William Herschel: Pioneer of Sidereal Astronomy* (London and New York, 1959)

G. Buttmann, *Wilhelm Herschel, Leben und Werk*, (Stuttgart, 1961)

Index